3817

Donated to the Li...
Souther...

Withdrawn

2

THE
SOUTHDOWN SHEEP

THE
SOUTHDOWN SHEEP

*Published by the WEALD AND DOWNLAND OPEN AIR MUSEUM
on behalf of the SOUTHDOWN SHEEP SOCIETY in honour of
two centuries of the breed which JOHN ELLMAN was the
first to improve, and to celebrate the Society's Centenary*

Valerie Porter

THE WEALD AND DOWNLAND OPEN AIR MUSEUM

First published in 1991 by
the Weald and Downland Open Air Museum,
Singleton, Chichester, PO18 0EU
© Valerie Porter 1991
All rights reserved

Design and production by
John Wiley & Sons Ltd, Chichester

Typeset in 11/13 point Baskerville by
APS, Salisbury

Printed and bound in Great Britain by
Biddles Ltd, Guildford and King's Lynn

ISBN 0–905259–18–1

The publication of this centenary history of the Southdown has been made possible by the generous help of publishers John Wiley & Sons (Chichester), the Society of Sussex Downsmen, and West Sussex County Council, as well as individual members of the Southdown Sheep Society

Contents

Foreword

The Rt. Hon. the Lord Harvington of Nantwich

I have been asked to write a few words about our breed, the Southdown, as I have known it intimately during the first sixteen years following the war and by keeping in touch since.

I stumbled into the possession of my flock when I bought the estate of Hazleton Manor, between Tetbury and Cirencester. Part of the in-going was to take the Southdown flock, at valuation, which I did, and I immediately fell in love with them and their beauty.

Almost my first action was to attend a meeting at Chichester which, I think, had a lasting effect on the breed: a great debate took place as to whether we should aim for a larger animal or for quality and a smaller size. The proponents of the latter policy won the day and for a few years this decision was vital to our export trade to New Zealand and Australia. Sadly, this trade came to an end in 1951, when a ban was placed on the importation of rams into those countries owing to the disease of scrapie. By then, larger sheep were being called for by our own home trade and the type of sheep we had developed took some time to alter to suit the home market.

Personally, during the sixteen years I was a Southdown flock owner, I was very fortunate in having two remarkable shepherds, Mr Bone and Mr Adlem, whose knowledge and ability to present their sheep on the show line won many prizes for me.

I was particularly lucky in buying a ram lamb from Mr Michael

Dewar at his break-up sale, following the first Royal at Lincoln in 1948, and this ram was the main progenitor of my successful Hazleton line. The following year at York he was Supreme Champion, winning the Northumberland Cup, and his descendants won it five more times for me, finishing up three times running at the last three fixed Royal Shows before the Royal moved to Kenilworth and I gave up farming. When my son-in-law took over the farm, the flock had to go and that, unfortunately, was the end of it. The flock had brought me the greatest excitement and I was immensely proud of our success.

During all this time, I had been your working President twice and your representative on the National Sheep Breeders' Association, of which I also became President. I was steeped in the cause of sheep for all those lean years when the animal was very low down in the farming world in general and it has been a source of great pleasure to see the recovery over the years, watching the fields (as one moved about) filling with sheep where one never saw any before.

I made many friends amongst our Southdown fraternity, many of whom have now passed on but some, I am glad to say, are still with us. I shall never forget the visit to the Comte de Bouille's flock, which was one of the best Southdown flocks in France, and I remember well the kindness of our hosts and the interest of seeing how a top-class sheep show was run in France.

I am glad that we shall be celebrating our centenary year at a time when sheep have a more certain future than since the war. I end by wishing the breed, and all those who promote it today, the good fortune they deserve, for one way or another it produces the finest quality lamb, through its various crosses, that can be found.

HARVINGTON*

---

* Lord Harvington is better known to Southdown breeders as Wing Commander Sir Robert Grant-Ferris MP, former Deputy Speaker of the House of Commons and President of the Southdown Sheep Society in 1950–51, 1959 and 1973.

Introduction

John Thorley
Secretary of the National Sheep Association

In congratulating the Southdown Sheep Society upon achieving its centenary, it is perhaps an occasion to reflect upon parts of the role which the breed has played in lamb production across the world and also how much influence the officers and breeders have had upon my own organisation.

Looking at this latter part first, 1991 is the centenary of the Southdown Sheep Society and 1992 will be the centenary of the National Sheep Association, formerly the National Sheep Breeders' Association. Whilst our records were destroyed in the Second World War, Southdown breeders were involved in setting up the old NSBA and they shared a Secretary from 1891 to 1897. Involvement has continued right up until recent times, with Lord Harvington as the Association's President from 1956 to 1958 and Mr D. S. A. McDougall, a Southdown breeder and former President, becoming the first President of the reorganised NSA. Mr George Hughes, also a former President of the Southdowns, became an outstanding Chairman of NSA Council in the 1970s and is currently our only Vice-President. The present elder statesman of NSA Council is Mr Hugh Clark, whose guiding hand has kept us on the straight and narrow path for a good number of years. There will be many others whom I could name but these few suffice to establish the current close links which exist between our organisations, I believe for mutual benefit.

It is, however, the influence the Southdown breed has had on the sheep industry generally which I find the most fascinating. While it has had (and continues to have) a role as a terminal crossing sire to produce quality prime lamb, not only in this country but in most other countries where sheep meat is important, its role as a progenitor of other meat sires gives it a special place in the industry as a whole.

The breed which sires about half the UK lamb production is the Suffolk, derived from the old Norfolk Horn and the Southdown. The Dorset Down benefited from a strong influence of Southdown blood. Recently, during the last twenty years or so, it is even more interesting to see that Mr Fell's Meatlinc benefited from both Suffolk and Dorset Down, while many of the meat sires imported from France during recent years have noticeably close relationships with the Southdown. It can therefore be said quite fairly that the Southdown plays a very significant part in today's sheep industry. I have no doubt whatsoever that it will continue to do so.

As we move towards the end of the second millenium, even more emphasis will be placed upon a high quality article to satisfy an increasingly discerning customer. The genetic make up of the Southdown and its many derivatives has always been valued by producers who pride themselves on their ability to breed a superior product. There is every indication that such confidence will, quite rightly, continue well into the foreseeable future.

JOHN THORLEY
Secretary General, National Sheep Association

CHAPTER ONE

The South Downs and their Sheep

> The South Downs, in agricultural language, is a body of hill and vale in the county of Sussex, extending from Eastbourne on the East to Shoreham River on the West, they afford support to nearly 150,000 sheep, from which nearly 100,000 lambs are reared annually. The herbage of the South Downs, it is understood, consists principally of wild thyme, burnet, yarrow, trefoil and eyebright. [Edmund Scott, 1798]

The South Downs run right across southern Sussex from the Hampshire border in the west to Beachy Head in the east, a distance of some sixty miles, and they are at most five or six miles wide, lifting their weather-rounded chalk bulk suddenly but smoothly above the flat, wet, oak-studded claylands of the Weald which fill much of the lowland plains to the north.

The Downs have always protected the secret afforested Weald, though here and there this natural line of defence against the sea and seaborne invaders is breached by south-flowing rivers — the Arun, the Adur and the Ouse. Small villages dot the hemline at the foot of the steep contours on the Downs' northern faces; a few larger villages and towns take advantage of the river valleys and more particularly the mild maritime climate on the southern coastal plains, but high up on the Downs, even today, there is only a scattering of hidden farms and the reminders left by ancient races — tumuli, flints, Neolithic hill camps, earthworks, tracks baring the chalk, yew groves and skyline tree circles.

These uplands, the home of skylarks, orchids, blue butterflies, wild thyme and rabbits, formed a cradle for the Southdown, a sturdy, thrifty breed of sheep perfectly adapted to the short, springy, sweet pastures that managed to grow from the thin soil which veiled the chalk and its flint stones. Originally a small native heath sheep of considerable hardiness, dark-faced and hornless, the Southdown had the good fortune to be chosen for development more than two hundred years ago by Sussex's master breeder, John Ellman. The Southdown became the founder and improver of a whole family of shortwool downland sheep throughout Britain (and overseas as well), parallel in influence and almost in time to the equally famous Dishley Leicester longwool of Robert Bakewell.

In the eighteenth century it was declared by Sir John Sinclair that the perfect sheep would have a Merino fleece, a Bakewell carcase and the Southdown's constitution but, in the absence of such an ideal combination in a single breed, the Southdown's hardiness and adaptability gave it first place among British sheep. These three breeds — Southdown, Leicester and Merino — have played major roles in the development of sheep breeds throughout the world.

This book, published to commemorate the centenary of the foundation of the Southdown Sheep Society, celebrates also John Ellman and above all celebrates the sheep that he transformed two centuries ago from a local type with a very long history to a fine-woolled, early-maturing prime lamb sire with a future as great as its famous past. Ellman claimed that it was more difficult to maintain a good breed than to raise it to first class and he has bequeathed to today's breeders the challenge of continuing what he began.

CHAPTER TWO

Portrait of the Southdown

The traditional Southdown is the smallest of the Down breeds but its size can be deceptive. It is a beautifully proportioned sheep with a comfortably chunky body, supported squarely on quite short, straight legs. It has a broad, level back and famously meaty rump and thighs that are a butcher's delight. Its dense wool is the shortest among the British sheep (save for the almost naked Wiltshire Horn) and is the finest in the country; it covers the entire body, down to the knees and hocks, and most of the face except around the large, bright, kind eyes and over the bridge of the nose. The exposed areas of the teddy-bear face and the lower legs are a soft, even, light mousy grey-brown, a colour which is a trademark of the breed. Its head is neat and quite small but broad and level between the short-woolled ears and its expression reflects its renowned amenability, though its general attitude and carriage are lively — 'the carriage of a gentleman and the walk of a thoroughbred,' they used to say. It is a sheep that looks well satisfied and indeed is one of the easiest to please and control. Some say that a Southdown will rarely take advantage of a gate carelessly left ajar, and the cost of confining it is minimal.

That affability has been developed over several centuries by the traditional local practice of folding the sheep over quite small areas so that the flocks were familiar with their shepherds and quite accustomed to regular herding and handling. The Southdown is still a positive pleasure to keep and is the original 'easy-care' sheep.

Its main role today is as a terminal sire for prime crossbred lambs. The high quality of its carcase has been a hallmark for two centuries and, as a strongly prepotent breed, the ram's carcase qualities are firmly stamped on its progeny, along with its well-known early maturity which allows a quick turnover in lamb production. These qualities, along with its traditional ability to thrive even when its environment is difficult and to be more tightly stocked than other breeds, are described in greater detail in a later section devoted to the breed's commercial value today. However, here is a random selection of quotations which help to build up a picture of the Southdown.

> Their activity resembles the hare, and points to the mountains as their home. Their wool being closely fitted to their backs (being tight and firm, resisting wet and cold) makes them well adapted to cold climates. [John Ellman, 1780s]

> Between Bourne and Steyning, which is 33 miles, the Downs are about six miles wide, and in this tract there are, it is said, about 200,000 ewes kept. I am inclined to think that this is (the soil considered) the highest stocking that is known in this kingdom, and ought to give us a good opinion of the Breed that can be kept in such numbers on a given space of country ... In all respects the Southdown is an exceptional Breed, and this is proved beyond all doubt, from the fact that farmers keep them at the rate of $1\frac{1}{2}$ to the acre. [Arthur Young, 1788]

> The Southdown is distinctly the smallest of the Down breeds and attains, at maturity, less than two-thirds of the weight of the Lincoln. The leg of mutton is remarkably thick and heavy. The wool is short, dense, and very fine, commanding the top price per pound for British wools. For quality of meat the breed is unsurpassed, and as a winner of carcass competitions it occupies a place comparable to that of the Aberdeen-Angus among cattle. The lambs mature and fatten very early and produce small fleshy joints with very little bone. [*Agriculture: The Science and Practice of British Farming*, Watson and More, 1944]

> There are no more beautiful sheep to look at than purebred South-downs, with their neat, compact bodies, on short legs, their close and thick fleeces of high quality wool, their shapely heads, and faces of mouse-brown colour, their well-filled legs of mutton, and their active, aristocratic carriage. [*The Southdown Sheep*, edited by E. Walford Lloyd, 1946]

The Southdown breed, whose foundations Ellman so well and truly laid, became and remains to this day the ideal butcher's sheep, with minimum waste, and maximum development of the cuts consumers prefer ... As a pre-potent sire to stamp the finest quality on lambs, the Southdown ram has few serious rivals ... It is both interesting and noteworthy that the Southdown — the world's premier mutton sheep — also carries the finest and most valuable fleece of any English sheep breed — a sufficient answer to those who contend that good flesh and good wool cannot come from the same sheep ... The export record of the leading English Southdown flocks is unsurpassed by that of any other breed. [Allan Fraser, DSc, MD, *Sheep Husbandry and Diseases*, 1957]

The thoroughbred horse, the Berkshire hog and the Southdown sheep are the only farm animals known that can properly be called thoroughbred. [Judge T. C. Jones of Delaware, Ohio]

The Southdown has always been regarded as the 'quality' sheep par excellence. It has proved itself in the carcase competitions so often that it is surprising that other breeds are used at all. [*The Southdown*, Southdown Sheep Society of New Zealand, 1971]

From a breeder's point of view, the Southdown is the better sheep because of its ability to do in hard times and its ease of lambing. We always have more Southdown lambs [than Dorsets] under equal conditions and the Southdown lambs are up and suckling a lot quicker. [Tom McCormack of Crookwell, Australia, commercial breeder, 1989]

One of the great breeds of British live stock, known the world over, with a history full of championships from Smithfield to Chicago ... It brought into favour the small joint of delicious flavour, it produced wool of fine texture commanding top price, and it supplies a dash — sometimes a splash — of blood to many other Down breeds to their advantage. [Farmer & Stockbreeder, 1940s]

The Southdown is one of the great sheep of history. [*Sheep of the World*, Kenneth Ponting, 1980]

CHAPTER THREE

The Development of the Southdown

CONTEXT FOR THE MASTER BREEDERS

Any notable development in agriculture needs to be seen in the context of the social environment that precipitated or encouraged it. Agriculture is specifically a response to human needs on a broad scale, however local or apparently selfish the immediate motive might seem. John Ellman, born in the middle of the eighteenth century, reacted to a current situation in England and probably had very little idea that he was in fact a standard bearer for a revolution.

As the eighteenth century dawned, agricultural practices were still medieval. Typically, the land was farmed on a three-course rotation: in the first year a winter grain crop, in the second a spring crop of corn, oats, barley, beans or peas, followed by a fallow year during which livestock grazed whatever the land might chance to throw up. In such a system, winter fodder was so scarce that most livestock were slaughtered when the grazing faded in late autumn and the meat was salted down for the winter — hence a positive plethora of feast-days and fairs at that time of year. The animals which had not been slaughtered were necessarily hardy and thrifty (and usually small) if they were to survive the short-rations winter. The basic ability to survive was far more important than productivity or form, and breeding was more a matter of natural rather than artificial selection. The survivors became the breeders.

Local types of livestock had developed, representing mainly those well enough adapted to local conditions and, gradually, those that appealed because of their coat colour perhaps, or their suitability for work or for production to meet local needs. Travel was limited so that livestock generally developed in some isolation and began to form quite uniform local populations, almost by chance. It was not until later in the eighteenth century, and more dramatically in the nineteenth, that livestock began to be bred more specifically to meet certain requirements, both in outward appearance and in production.

At the end of the seventeenth century, the population of England was about 6 million. Population centres were relatively small and there was ample land around them (and within them) for farming to meet local needs at a time when the difficulties and costs of transport considerably impeded the movement of agricultural produce. But during the eighteenth century there were several major and interlinked revolutions which changed the face of the nation.

From the agricultural point of view, the main spur to development was the human population explosion: from 1764 to 1826, the population increased by more than 75%, and there was a massive migration of people into towns and cities, precipitated by an industrial revolution that created large manufacturing centres. The concentration of a landless population, unable to produce food for itself, placed great demands on agriculture and encouraged a rapid evolution from local self-sufficiency to larger-scale production for the export of surpluses to the cities. This huge and sudden agricultural revolution was initiated by a handful of farsighted and imaginative but thoroughly practical agriculturalists.

Jethro Tull, born in 1674, developed his seed-drill; Charles Townshend, born in the same year, introduced the humble but in its own way revolutionary turnip. Townshend gave new lease to the land by replacing fallows with root crops and clover grazing, thus providing winter fodder for livestock that in turn manured the ground as they fed on the roots in the field so that the soil was enriched for future crops and its grain-growing potential was manifoldly augmented. Because large numbers of animals could now be retained throughout the winter, the available manure increased substantially and therefore the land gave even more grain, fodder and grazing, and the upward spiral continued.

The time was ripe for not only increasing but also improving the nation's livestock now that the pool of genetic material was expanding. The arable men paved the way for the master animal breeders.

An important strand in the breeding tapestry was the land enclosures of the period. When herds and flocks were communally grazed, it was almost impossible (and anyway rarely considered necessary) to

John Ellman of Glynde 1753–1832.

practise selective breeding. Mating was random, as it always had been. Robert Bakewell and John Ellman were unusual for their time in that they deliberately selected their breeding stock from the best animals available to them and then set about breeding for specific qualities. Bakewell, born in 1725, wanted sheep and cattle that fattened easily and economically, and he practised careful inbreeding to fix his preferred Dishley types of Leicester sheep and Longhorn cattle. Down in East Sussex John Ellman, born in 1753, worked with different stock and with different aims: he wanted a well-balanced sheep suited to downland conditions which would rapidly and thriftily produce a good leg of mutton—the more expensive cut, as he had noted at the butcher's. He looked for pleasing proportions, a fine, short, dense fleece and early maturity. His downland sheep would become a major influence in the nineteenth century during the rush of formal breed establishment of that period.

Not only was Ellman the original developer of the Southdown breed but also, along with Bakewell, he had a major influence on sheep-breeding techniques in Britain and thus also throughout the English-speaking world. Both men, destined to be rivals though born almost a generation apart, were thoroughly practical farmers and husbandmen first and foremost. Their breeding techniques were based on a sound knowledge of the land as well as livestock, and they knew that even a good breed — or perhaps especially so — needed good husbandry and appropriate feeding to achieve its proper potential. Ellman's management methods are as interesting as his breeding techniques and are therefore given in some detail in a later section: they are of a past age but are not irrelevant to modern shepherding.

First, however, what about Ellman the breeder and Ellman the man?

JOHN ELLMAN (1753–1832)

Although it has been told many times, Ellman's own story is integral to the history of the Southdown and it is therefore briefly repeated here. It is given in greater detail in *The Southdown Sheep* (published in several editions since 1922 by the Southdown Sheep Society) and at considerable length in the 'Memoir of Mr Ellman' reproduced in Baxter's *Library of Agricultural & Horticultural Knowledge*.

Ellman was a man of great generosity and was commended not only for his superb sheep-breeding but also for his role in public life and in agricultural life in general. In 1834, two years after his death, the introduction to the third edition of Baxter's splendid compilation, admittedly perhaps a little prejudiced, stated:

> Other names may shine more conspicuously in the pages of scientific biography, or the records of busy history: — a memoria of JOHN ELLMAN will not unfold curious discoveries to the speculative philosopher, nor display stirring incidents to the lover of exciting adventure; but it will present a more useful, though less imposing prospect — the undeviating and successful devotion of an honest and honourable man to a pursuit, alike essential to the well-being of the community and the power of the state. A full and complete life of Mr Ellman would ... comprise a progressive history of English Agriculture during the last sixty years, for with every association or society formed for the improvement of cattle, the advancement of agricultural knowledge, and the reward of labouring industry, he was intimately connected — and from his exertions, indeed, most of them derived their existence.

Richard and Elizabeth Ellman's son John was born on 17 October 1753, at the village of Hartfield near East Grinstead in north Sussex, on the upper reaches of Kent's River Medway. Richard continued to farm at Hartfield until 1761 when he took his family to Place Farm or Great Farm at Glynde, three miles east of the East Sussex town of Lewes, and he died at Glynde in 1780. Three years later John married Elizabeth Spencer and in 1787 she bore him a son (also named John) who would succeed his father as the third generation of Ellmans at Glynde nearly half a century hence. Elizabeth died just before Christmas in 1790 and John married his second wife, Constantia Davis, daughter of the Vicar of Glynde, in 1794. This marriage lasted for nearly forty years and they had several children.

Glynde was well placed: it had the Wealden winter grazing lands close by where store sheep were welcome; it was accessible to London's fatstock markets, and the nearby River Ouse was navigable up to Lewes for the transport of grain and other produce. In 1780 Ellman's farm grew 150 acres of wheat and had another 150 acres of downland and 200 acres of 'brookland' or water-meadow grazing.

Richard Ellman had known a great deal about farming, especially as a grazier, and recognised the importance of careful book-keeping. However, he had little faith in book-learning, deeming it more valuable for his son to learn 'in the field', and young John had only two winter quarters in the schoolroom. As he said later, 'I have spent more time between the plough handles than in a grammar school'. However, as a young man he was helped to improve his reading by the vicar who would become his second father-in-law. John was an articulate, intelligent and fluent man with a keen desire to publicise the breed he improved, which made very good commercial sense.

Richard Ellman had established a sound business in buying and selling sheep and cattle and in stock-keeping for other farmers, and John, even before his father's death, had begun the improvement of the Southdown, a sheep which, in his own words,

> was formerly of a small size, and far from possessing a good shape, being long and thin in the neck, high on the shoulders, low behind, high on the loins, down on the rumps, the tail set on very low, nearly perpendicular from the hip bones, sharp on the back, ribs flat, narrow in the fore-quarters, good in the leg with big bone.

They were also 'tub-bellied' and seldom fattened until four years old; seven stone was considered a great weight for a two-year-old South-down wether.

These small, active, short-woolled native heath sheep with dark faces, short speckled legs, a white tuft of wool on the forehead and no horns, had been run on the South Downs 'from time immemorial' — a loose phrase claimed by many a breed but such sheep had certainly been on the Downs for several centuries and, some claimed, since before the Roman invasion. They were predominant on the Downs to the east of the River Adur (which meets the south coast at Shoreham-by-Sea) and in type were in sharp contrast to the white-faced, horned sheep to the west of the Bramber and Beeding valley. The eastern sheep were grassland animals and were generally left to roam the Downs quite freely during the day but in due course the practice was to fold them overnight on small areas so that their manure was concentrated where it was needed. The poor chalk soils were hungry for enrichment.

In 1776 the English agricultural writer Arthur Young (1741–1820), who had unfortunately ruined his own large East Anglian farm after a series of experiments but who later became the first Secretary to the Board of Agriculture and was one of the first to make agriculture a science, spoke rather slightingly of the South Downs sheep which Ellman was about to improve:

> 'Fine wool is certainly a very considerable object, provided it is gained on a well-formed carcase; but if a fine coat is procured at the expense of a

thin chine, low fore-end, and rising back-bone, the advantage is purchased too dearly. The faults most common in the South Down breed are these three. They are found very general even in the best flocks, inasmuch as not more than one sheep in a hundred, perhaps in two hundred, is to be seen tolerably free from them.

However, the sheep thrived locally and some of the best downland wool was being produced between Brighton and Eastbourne by 1780. Ellman probably began improving the native type in about 1778 and ten years later Young visited Glynde while compiling the *Annals of Agriculture*, a major work in the form of a journal recording his countrywide tours on a blind white horse — the pair covered 20 000 miles from 1783 onwards. He described the true, wellbred 'South Down' of 1788 in the following terms:

No horns; a long speckled face; clean and thin jaw; a long but not a thin neck; no tuft of wool on the forehead, which they call owl-headed, nor any frizz of wool on the cheeks; thick in the shoulder; open-breasted and deep; both fore and hind legs stand wide; round and straight in the barrel; wide upon the loin and hips; shut well in the twist, which is a projection of flesh on the inner part of the thigh, that gives a fulness when viewed behind, and makes a South Down leg of mutton remarkably round and short, more so than in most other breeds; thin speckled leg and free from wool; the belly full of wool; the wool close and hard to the feel, curdled to the eye, and free from spiry, projecting, or staring fibres. Those flocks not bred with particular care and attention are apt to be coarse-woolled in the breech, but some are fine all over; weigh, fat, from twelve to eighteen pounds a quarter ... The wool is the finest in England, the Hereford alone excepted; the mutton has no superior, and in hot weather is much better than the Norfolk, and they are constantly folded — all three points of the first importance.

But the merit of every species of live stock depends, in a considerable measure, on a point that has for centuries been unaccountably neglected, and that is, the quantity of food eaten, which will depend greatly on those points of form which are connected with or occasion hardiness; it is an observation in which experienced sheep-masters in most countries will agree, that a flat back without ridge, and a broad loin and thick carcass, with a close hard-woolled coat, will stand the vicissitudes of bad weather and hard food much better than a thin carcass, a narrow loin, and an open loose-woolled one. Compare sheep in the same flock, and on the same food, — those that are well formed in these respects will, at a pinching season, be in better order than others that are thus worse made;

and a sheep having a disposition to do kindly and to be in good order and fat, is a circumstance second to none, always supposing that the breed, whatever it is, is saleable. In all these respects the South Down is an unexceptionable breed; — what I have just explained that the farmers possessed of them on farms, the average rent of which all through is about 12s., keep at the rate of one and a half per acre, seems to put this matter beyond all doubt. I know of no lands in the kingdom, rich marshes excepted, which are stocked in such a proportion; for it is not to be forgotten, that on every one of these farms there is a considerable stock of horned cattle kept — cows, calves, succession beasts, plough oxen and fatted ones ... Such quantities of live stock as are on the Down farms render the arable exceedingly productive, and assists very much (for goodness of soil does not the whole) in giving them products much superior to any thing we know, with more correct management.

Thus the Southdown already showed its wool quality, its promising leg of mutton and its ability to be tightly stocked and thrifty. Young, a wise and well-travelled observer, was able to declare from the evidence of his own flocks in Norfolk that Southdown sheep of the same weight ate less than Norfolks and were 'at the same time in better order' but that the 'gross ignorance and inveterate prejudice of shepherds, who, in every country, are so bigoted to their own breed, that they are sure to declare war against every innovation' and whose masters were 'either as prejudiced as themselves, or too idle to attempt to overcome petty difficulties' would make it difficult to introduce the admirable improved Southdown breed to regions other than Sussex and Kent.

In fact, as early as the 1780s Ellman's sheep were being sold to Essex (Lord Waldegrave), Nottinghamshire and Norfolk, and flocks were established by the Duke of Grafton and by Francis, 5th Duke of Bedford, at Woburn. In 1800 his rams went to Northumberland, in 1801 to Ireland, in 1803 to Scotland — and in the 1790s to Russia. By the end of the eighteenth century many of the breed were seen in gentlemen's parks in northern England.

Young clearly had considerable respect for the sheep and particularly for the breeder John Ellman, whom he first met through their mutual acquaintance, the Earl of Sheffield, of Sheffield Place in Sussex. 'There is nothing,' said Young, writing of his tour of Sussex in the late 1780s, 'in which this very active farmer is more praiseworthy than in the attention he has given to improve the breed. There is hardly a greater object than this, let the breed be what it may; if very bad it admits of infinite improvement, and if very good it may be made better. In the general management of his farm Mr Ellman is attentive, and intelligent in the motives of his conduct. His business is not an inconsiderable one.'

At that time, the Glynde farm's 580 acres supported 700 ewes, a score of Sussex cows and a bull, 122 other cattle (youngstock, working oxen and fatteners) and half a dozen cart horses. Indeed, Young asked in 1791 why 'this most intelligent and successful breeder of sheep' had not given equal attention to cattle — and within six years Ellman had become almost as well known for his red Sussex oxen as for his Southdown sheep. Lord Egremont reported the observation of an experienced racehorse breeder who had said that if Ellman would only apply his expertise to horse flesh 'and *be a little less open and honest*', he would 'beat all the men he knew'.

However, the sheep continued to be his prime interest and for the sake of his sheep and cattle Ellman also made strides in improving arable yields for fodder crops. In 1792 he renewed the tenancy on Place

Shearling ewe bred and exhibited by John Ellman, 1798. This is one of the earliest known illustrations of a Southdown, showing the speckled face of the original heath type.

Farm and leased an additional 120 acres of brookland so that the holding became 700 acres in all. In the same year he became steward of several other Sussex estates belonging to his landlords, the Trevors, yet somehow found time to accompany Young on a tour of Romney Marsh and East Kent.

In 1794 Young described the breed as 'small but compact, containing a great weight in small compass' and praised Ellman's flock as 'unquestionably the first in the country. There is nothing that can be compared with it; the wool the finest, and the carcase the best proportioned.' This 'incomparable' and 'admirable' farmer, said Young, had improved the native Southdown sheep without recourse to crossing to other breeds: it was a true thoroughbred. His praise waxed increasingly lyrical.

> The South Down breed of sheep is sufficiently domesticated for hill sheep, — a breed that requires but little activity to fill themselves on hard and short keep, between the hours of turning them out of the fold in the morning and putting them into it again at night, — a practice very general throughout this country. The colour of their legs and faces are generally grey or speckled; clean small bone; carcass tolerably straight and wide; they stand rather higher behind than before, which, by some, has been particularly objected to. Mr Ellman observes that he cannot as yet satisfy himself of the impropriety of it: they are thicker in their hind than in their fore quarters, and, when fat, the hind quarters are frequently 2 lb or 3 lb per quarter heavier than the fore; in which case, Mr Ellman perfectly agrees with Mr Bakewell, as the true criterion of breeding is flesh, and not bone, on the most valuable part of the animal ... The mutton is allowed to be equal to the best in the island, and the wool little, if at all, inferior to the Hereford ... No other breed of sheep is more healthy and hardy than this, and from the closeness of the wool are well defended against the beating winds and rain; they naturally possess, likewise, a good constitution.

By 1803 Ellman's flock numbered 1708 (including 403 flock ewes) and in 1808 his shepherd Charles Payne raised 799 lambs from 600 ewes, having lost only 21.

In Baxter, naturally, the praise of Ellman and his sheep is high throughout, even to the extent of denigrating, by comparison, the character of that other famous breeder, Robert Bakewell of Dishley who, it was claimed, was far from generous with his expertise and a man of 'narrow jealousies', whereas Ellman 'disclosed all his successive

Two-shear ram bred and exhibited by John Ellman, 1798.

discoveries in the mode of breeding with unreserved frankness, and carried on all his operations openly before the eye of any spectator who might please to witness them. A generous communicativeness was, from youth to old age, a part of Mr Ellman's character . . . ' However, Sue Farrant, in her article on Ellman in the *Agricultural History Review* (Vol. 26, 1978), gives the man more human qualities by suggesting that he was perhaps not wholly altruistic: good publicity for the breeder sold more of his sheep.

It was an exciting period for livestock breeding in a time of agricultural prosperity and Ellman, 'without hereditary connections, without education, without inherited wealth or descended honours,' found himself frequently in the company of gentlemen, who clamoured for his advice and bought his sheep. The Ellman story is littered with noble names, not only in England but also in Ireland. Among the former were his long-time supporter the Duke of Bedford, with an excellent flock at Woburn, and Thomas W. Coke of Holkham Hall in Norfolk, later to be the Earl of Leicester. Both held famous sheep-shearings at their respective estates, and here, as Baxter describes it, 'nobles, gentlemen and labourers met together, and all profited by the union; where the moral feelings of him who sheared the fleece were exalted by the sympathy and personal attention of his master, and the friendly communion of Royal Princes.'

Yet Ellman retained his integrity and never forgot that he was above all a farmer — a practical farmer. His husbandry and breeding were always most careful and diligent. For the most part he was probably no more original or advanced than other well informed sheep farmers of the time but he was a good communicator of his knowledge, and that perhaps was the secret of the success of his sheep. There is little point in having a magnificent breed if no one else is aware of its qualities.

After his second marriage in 1794, when he was in his early forties, Ellman became more involved in public affairs, initially directly connected with farming — for example wool fairs, and agricultural associations to encourage improved breeding. He was a founder member of the Sussex Agricultural Society at Lewes, which thrived in the 1790s though it later crumbled because of bickering among its members. In 1798 Ellman, the Duke of Bedford and the Leicester breeder Astley instituted the Smithfield Society and its Cattle Show in London, a show which is still of great importance nearly two centuries later.

Education, the poor laws, tithes, tree ownership, taxes — many subjects attracted Ellman's attention and he become Justice of the Peace and Deputy Lieutenant for Sussex, meanwhile refusing a baronetcy and peerage. As early as 1780 he had become actively involved with the improvement of the River Ouse and the adjacent 4000 acres of the Lewes and Laughton levels and in 1782 he became a Commissioner of Newhaven Harbour.

His efforts, both as an agricultural improver and as a public benefactor and activist, were appreciated and frequently acknowledged. In 1800, for example, twenty-seven of Sussex's principle landowners and nobility presented him with an inscribed silver cup engraved with a portrait of his two-year-old prize-winning ram; in 1805 the Duke of Bedford personally presented him with an inscribed silver vase; and in 1819 the Board of Agriculture, no doubt through the recommendations of Arthur Young, awarded him a gold medal for the best cultivated farm in Sussex.

The fame of the breeder and his sheep spread overseas as well and the Emperor of Russia ordered two Ellman rams through His Majesty

King George III in 1798. Ellman was introduced to the King the following year by Lord Somerville, who had imported Merino sheep from Lisbon to improve British wool. The King presented Ellman with ten Merino ewes and two rams from his own flock at Kew, though Ellman later abandoned the Merinos 'because of the difficulty I had in selling them in a lean state. The graziers did not want them, and I then tried to fatten them myself, but I found I could fatten *three* Southdowns where I could only fatten *one* Merino. I treated them as I would other sheep, but I could never fatten one of them well.'

Somerville had a special interest in the manufacture of fine cloth from home-produced wool and in 1800 he told Ellman: 'I continue, as usual, to go into and out of people's rooms without being turned out, but I also find the kerseymere a pleasant wear. Long live the South Downs!' His enthusiasm spread among his contemporaries. In 1814, for example, the Earl of Bridgewater gave Ellman a piece of blue broadcloth made from the wool of his own Southdowns, and on 28 June 1811, Sir John Throckmorton won a thousand-guinea bet by sitting down to dine in the evening in a damson-coloured suit made from Southdown wool which had been shorn from the sheep at sunrise that very morning. The wager involved John Coxeter, a prosperous cloth manufacturer at Greenham Mills, Newbury, who commissioned a local artist (Luke Clint) to commemorate the event in a large oil painting. The Royal Agricultural Society of England gave Coxeter a congratulatory medal and the event was described thus:

> On the day above stated at 5 o'clock in the morning Sir John Throckmorton presented 2 South Down Sheep to Mr Coxeter of Greenham Mills near Newbury, Berkshire. The Sheep were immediately shorn, the Wool sorted and spun, the Yarn spool'd, warp'd, loom'd & wove. The Cloth burr'd, mill'd, row'd, dy'd, dry'd, shear'd and pressed. The Cloth having been thus made in 11 hours was put into the Hands of the Tailors at 4 o'Clock in the afternoon who completed the Coat at 20 minutes past 6. Mr Coxeter then presented the Coat to Sir John Throckmorton who appeared with it the same Evening at the Pelican Inn, Speenhamland. The Cloth was a hunting Kersey of the admired Wellington Colour: The Sheep were roasted whole & distributed to the Public with 120 Gallons of Strong Beer; It was supposed that upwards of 5,000 people were assembled to witness this Singular and unprecedented performance, which was completed in the space of 13 hours and 20 mintues. Sir John and about 40 Gentlemen sat down to a dinner

provided by Mr Coxeter and spent the Evening with the utmost satisfaction at the success of their undertaking.

A piece of the Throckmorton coat cloth was exhibited at the RASE's exhibition 'This Land is Our Land' in the Mall Galleries in January 1989, and a note attached to it explained that ten tailors had been employed in the challenge. In its centenary year in 1991 the Southdown Sheep Society hopes to re-enact the achievement but intends to take a more leisurely two days to do so.

Many of the manufacturers actively supported the woolgrowers and encouraged their efforts to improve fleeces at that time. Wool quality was of particular interest to Ellman, whose Southdown wool was the nearest English fleece to the Merino, and he deliberately fed his flock 'on a diet which did not diminish the fineness of the wool, while it fattened the carcase.' He disagreed with the common belief that an increase in quantity led inevitably to a decrease in quality and he sought to improve both, as well as the carcase under the fleece.

In 1829 John Ellman decided to retire. His flock was auctioned and the tributes, written and spoken, came pouring in. 186 noblemen and gentlemen had their names inscribed on a huge, ornamental silver tureen surmounted by the figure of a Southdown sheep, which was presented to the breeder in August that year. The full inscription read:

To
JOHN ELLMAN, OF GLYNDE, ESQ.
on his retiring from the Farm,
in which, for more than half a century, he had devoted himself
TO THE INTERESTS OF AGRICULTURE,
As a Token of their sincere regard,
and a Tribute to his great merit,
especially in improving and extending throughout
THE BRITISH EMPIRE
THE BREED OF SOUTH DOWN SHEEP,
and his much admired conduct
TO HIS LABOURERS,
This Piece of Plate is presented,
By a number of Agriculturists and Friends;
And to his Family,
A Portrait of Himself.

Sitting for that portrait caused Ellman such irritation that he became ill! Hence the picture's air of severity, which is quite out of character.

After his retirement, Ellman lived alternately at Lewes and at his small High Cross estate near Uckfield. He died at his Lewes house, quite suddenly, on 22 November 1832, and was buried in the family vault at Glynde. His son John succeeded him at Glynde, from which his flock of 1350 head was dispersed in 1846. Another son, Thomas, based his own Beddingham flock on Glynde stock and his 690 head were dispersed in 1867. The last flock in the Ellman family — the Landport — was sold by R. H. Ellman in 1876 (980 head) and it, too, was descended from original Glynde stock.

Glynde Place is now the home of Viscount Hampden and in September 1991 it is the focal point of the Southdown Sheep Society's centenary celebrations. John Ellman's grave in Glynde churchyard has been restored by craftsmen in the last few years with the help of donations to a fund raised by the Society, which continues to maintain the grave. It was cleaned to a gleaming white in 1982 and the inscription, which was re-cut at the same time, reads:

> In the Vault below rest the remains of the late JOHN ELLMAN ESQ. Deputy Lieutenant and in the Commission of the Peace for this County. By him the breed of South Down sheep was first improved and thro his exertions spread over the whole Kingdom. A great portion of his life was spent rendering practical assistance to public improvements; at the same time he did not forget to promote the welfare and happiness of inhabitants of this Parish in which he resided for more than 60 years. He died 22nd Novr 1832 in the 80th year of his age.

THOMAS WILLIAM COKE, EARL OF LEICESTER
(1752–1842)

Coke of Norfolk, or Coke of Holkham, as he is often remembered, was almost the same age as John Ellman. From 1776 until his death in 1842 he owned Holkham Hall, built by his uncle Thomas (1697–1759) on the north Norfolk coast near Wells-next-the-Sea. Coke's Home Farm was a famous centre for agricultural improvements of many kinds and this well-known Whig was created the Earl of Leicester of Holkham in 1837.

Coke first took an interest in Southdown sheep in 1791 or 1792, when Ellman sent him 500 ewes and lambs and 4 of his best rams. Two years later Coke commissioned Arthur Young to purchase another 220 ewes and ewe lambs for his flock in Norfolk, including 100 Shoreham ewes. Soon he had 2500 Southdowns flourishing on an acreage where previously 800 Norfolks had been kept with difficulty.

Coke was a larger-than-life character and, like many of his contemporaries, relished a good bet. He wagered £500 to the Leicester Society to stock 100 acres with Southdown wethers against another 100 acres stocked by 'any four New Leicester breeders' but the society did not take up his challenge. In 1798 he offered a wager on behalf of the Southdowns at a time when 'the celebrity which the Southdown sheep long since obtained, they still maintain, at this period, indeed, there is a sort of rivalship, which has sprung up between the Southdown and the new Leicester, which though it is likely to end in the improvement of both, is not very likely to prove that the new Leicester is preferable to the old Southdown,' as the Sussex Agricultural Society put it.

Originally, Coke kept the local Norfolk Horn, a thrifty, long-lived, roving and somewhat scrawny sheep which he described as a 'vile degenerate breed', and he experimented with Bakewell's Leicesters and with Southdown rams to try to improve the Norfolk's meat production. The modern Suffolk was developed from the Southdown/Norfolk cross and was recognised as a breed in its own right in 1859. The cross was so successful that many Norfolk breeders adopted it and a few kept pure Southdowns instead of the old Norfolks. The Leicester was introduced at Holkham first (before 1784) but Coke switched to Southdowns once Ellman had visited him in the early 1790s, though in fact the first Southdowns came to Norfolk from Houghton in 1789. Ellman's visit, in July 1792, had been in the company of J. Boys of Betshanger in Kent (whose daughter would one day marry Ellman's son John) and Boys wrote a most enthusiastic report on their Holkham tour, full of glowing praise for Coke and his wife.

In 1778 Coke initiated his annual Holkham Sheep-shearings, or 'Coke's Clippings' as they were known locally, established to improve sheep breeding by exhibiting and comparing the fleeces and carcases of different breeds and giving local farmers an opportunity to hear and discuss Coke's latest theories. He made sure that his own rams were available for letting. The major Clippings took place from 1800 to 1821, the Southdown gaining popularity over the Leicester until by 1817 none of the latter was left. Merinos were also available from 1805 to 1811. At the last of the Clippings (the forty-third) the eighty house-guests included three dukes, ten lords and knights, and high-powered representatives from France, America, Poland, Russia, Sweden and Nova Scotia, while on each of the three public days up to 700 guests were entertained to dinner. They came not only for the social occasion but also to tour Coke's farms, see and discuss his improvements and innovations, watch demonstrations of crafts such as flax-spinning and witness the judging and prize-giving for fleeces and carcases. What a showcase for Ellman's Southdowns! The breed had become the favourite of the wealthy aristocracy.

In 1817 the Home Farm's flock boasted 996 Southdown ewes to a Southdown tup and by 1819 there were 1053. There were 30 000 acres at Holkham and it was said that Coke had filled the country with Whiggish sheep and spoiled the flavour of Norfolk mutton. He was most persuasive in 'encouraging' his tenants to farm Southdowns.

Coke, by then Earl of Leicester, died at Longford Hall, Derbyshire, and in 1845 a monument to him was put up in Holkham Park depicting Sheep-shearing scenes, irrigation schemes and other Coke activities and guarded by four statues representing his main interests: a seed drill, a plough, a Devon cow and a group of Southdown sheep. Today the Holkham estate still farms sheep, but they are, ironically perhaps, Border Leicester/Scottish Blackface crosses put to a Suffolk tup.

JONAS WEBB (1796–1862)

Towards the end of the eighteenth century Samuel Webb was farming at Harlaka Farm in Great Thurlow, Suffolk, until he came to Streetly Hall, West Wickham, near Cambridge, before the turn of the century. The holding consisted of 549 acres.

He had a large family, in more senses than one: there were nine sons and most of them stood more than six foot tall. The first was also named Samuel, who became known as the best farmer in the eastern counties and who made a habit of buying 'all the manure in Cambridge' and transporting it to his farm in dog-drawn carts. The second son, born a year later, was Jonas.

The boys' father experimented with various sheep breeds at Streetly and, it is said, young Jonas made an early decision in favour of the Southdown: he enjoyed riding his father's rams and found that the broad, level back of a Southdown was a great deal more comfortable

Jonas Webb of Babraham 1796–1862.

than the narrow, bony spine of the Norfolk Horn! Later he would claim
that he had been a ram rider before he became a ram breeder, and that
his early rides had determined him to breed broad-backed sheep. In
1845 he wrote more seriously about his choice in *The Farmers' Magazine*:

> I commenced breeding Southdown Sheep as soon as I began business for
> myself, about 22 years since, from a conviction, through many experi-
> ments made when at home with my father with many breeds of sheep,
> that more mutton and wool of the BEST QUALITY could be made per
> acre from Southdowns than from any other breeds, upon nine-tenths of
> the arable land in this country, where sheep are regularly folded,
> especially where the land is poor and the animals have far to walk to
> fold.
>   I commenced by purchasing the best bred sheep that I could obtain
> from the chief breeders in Sussex, regardless of expense, and I have never
> made a cross *from any other breed on any occasion since.*

It seems that Webb was in complete agreement on this point with
Ellman, who resolutely refused to cross his Southdown but improved it
by selective breeding within the breed instead. Webb also had strong
views on showing: he had won first prize for stock ewes and lambs at
the Royal in 1840 when it was held at Cambridge, but never again
showed his female stock for prizes, 'being convinced of the ruin
inevitably brought upon all breeding stock by overfeeding.' However,
he exhibited his rams widely and won most of the prizes at the Royal
for the next three years in succession, though he refused a huge sum for
the hire of two of his show rams because he believed that, being overfed
for exhibition purposes, they 'would not propagate'. This problem was
recorded by the American author, Elihu Burritt, who agreed with
Webb that 'a false condition of fat prevailed amongst all animals
obtaining prizes' at the annual exhibitions in England.

    Burritt wrote at some length about Jonas Webb. For example, he
described how his prize-winning streak with rams continued un-
checked, except on two occasions when his Southdowns failed to take
first place at Exeter in 1850 and at Chelmsford in 1856. On both
occasions Webb was convinced that the judges were wrong and he
quietly entered the same animals at other meetings (Windsor and
Salisbury respectively) where they took their deserved first prizes. In
1855 his sheep were the centre of attraction at the Paris Exhibition and
he presented his prize ram to Emperor Napoleon III as a gift — an

extravagant gesture but a very sound marketing move which resulted in Webb sheep promptly becoming much in demand in France.

In his early days Jonas Webb assisted Mr H. J. Adeane in the management of Babraham, a name which was to become synonymous with Webbs and Southdowns, and in 1820 he took over Church Farm on the Babraham estate. As manager, he travelled all over the country buying Southdowns for Adeane and he soon met John Ellman, purchasing some of his famous Glynde sheep and heeding his advice on the best types. It was a wise course to follow, and in 1842, when he exhibited at Dundee, the Highland Society took a likeness of his sheep as a prime example of the breed for its museum in Edinburgh.

Webb had clear ideas about the qualities he wished to fix in his Southdowns and, according to the *Cambridge Chronicle* (13 July 1886), 'the conviction first began to dawn on the agricultural mind that there was nothing like Mr Webb's breed of sheep for symmetry, wool and mutton about 1835.' By then Webb had established a system of annual ram-letting in July, when the rams were displayed with tickets indicating the fleece weight — an important factor for Webb, who concentrated on wool, size and constitution. His son Henry agreed with his father, saying, 'If you have the wool, you have the flesh. Good firm wool, and a nice medium colour were what Jonas Webb sought for, and he would not have them pale. He also liked a well covered head with a nice clear face and a good bright eye.'

Southdown rams bred by Jonas Webb and exhibited at the R.A.S. Meeting at Liverpool, July 1841.

Jonas Webb's rams were 'sent into every country in the civilised world' in due course, and Burritt said that it was difficult, if not impossible, to find a Southdown flock of any reputation in any country in the world not closely allied with the Babraham flock. More than 2000 people attended Webb's twelfth ram letting, and by the thirty-second such event the flock numbered 700 ewes and about 400 rams of various ages. In 1861, when the 65-year-old Webb dispersed his flock, about a thousand people sat down to lunch and 969 sheep were sold for a total of nearly £11 000, including a 'wonderful' ram to the American J. C. Taylor of Holmdale, New Jersey, and many sales to Canada, South America, Australia, New Zealand and many European countries. The ewes and ewe lambs were sold in 1862 and the final total was 1404 sheep sold for £16 646 14s 6d.

The RASE has a model of a four-year-old Webb ewe at its London offices. She was originally presented by Webb as a perfect specimen of the breed to Jonathan Thorne of New York and the scale model was sent to Webb in 1853. Jonathan Thorne's son Samuel, of Thornedale, Washington Hollow, in the New York county of Duchess (who also brought in the 'Duchess' Shorthorns from Lord Ducie's sale in 1853) imported from many of the best English flocks in the mid-nineteenth century, most of them Webb sheep or bred by Henry Lugar of Hengrave, Bury St Edmunds. It was Thorne sheep which formed the basis of the flock of General Cassius M. Clay at Whitehall Farm in Kentucky. Clay maintained his flock for more than fifty years, perpetuating Webb blood in America. The RASE model is accompanied by a handwritten note referring to Webb's transactions over the years and condensing his achievements into a chronological list, including sales to Paris, Portugal, Russia and Australia.

At its peak, the Babraham flock had numbered 2400 head and Webb believed that his greatest achievement was to prove to sceptics in East Anglia — and worldwide — that a sturdy type of Southdown could be reared not just on its natural, dry, chalk uplands but also on rich arable lowlands. It was indeed a most adaptable breed.

There were many parallels between Ellman and Webb: both were closely involved with the Smithfield Club, for example, and Webb was the first chairman of the Agricultural Hall Company. Webb, like Ellman, received many trophies and testimonials, perhaps the grandest being a magnificent solid silver candelabra, presented to Webb by the Emperor of France, in the fashion of an English oak whose branches

Statue of Jonas Webb, transferred to Babraham and re-erected by the Parish Council in 1981. John Bennett, chairman of Babraham Parish Council, with the Mayor of South Cambridgeshire. (*Cambridge Evening News*)

shaded a group of horses. Like Ellman, again, Webb also bred prize-winning horses (Suffolk Punches) and cattle (Shorthorns), and held many public offices.

Jonas Webb died on the day of his wife's funeral in November 1862. As a memorial to him, a large meeting of friends and admirers at the Agricultural Hall in London decided to erect a magnificent bronze statue in the Market Square at Cambridge, at a cost of £10000: subscriptions for it came from breeders and friends in many countries. The monument was later moved to the Corn Exchange but at last, in 1981, it was erected in the village of Babraham, where Jonas Webb and his wife were buried together. He had been described as 'an English farmer, the great type of the great race. He looks an English farmer — stalwart in form, of good countenance, hospitable to a fault; honest as a man can be; modest as true genius ever should display itself.'

Other Webb brothers also farmed Southdowns, including Samuel, who did well at Smithfield in the 1840s, and John of Horseheath, a notable 'character', standing six foot two and weighing 18 stone, a famous hunting man and smoker of good cigars. Jonas's own third son, also called Jonas, of Melton Ross in Lincolnshire, had a Southdown flock and also a flock of Lincoln Longwools, as well as a famous herd of Bates-type Shorthorn cattle based on the Babraham herd, and eventually there was a prize-winning herd of Lincoln Reds at Melton Ross.

HENRY WEBB

The great Jonas's eldest son, Henry, had lived at Streetly while helping his father at Babraham and, although the Babraham farms were given up when Jonas died, Henry bred Southdowns himself from 1856 until 1899. His flock was founded on Babraham blood and was augmented in 1861 with another seventy of the best ewes and ten rams from the Babraham dispersal sales. Henry's sheep were 'on a large scale, very short-legged with deep carcases, ... so high yet so low' with grand heads, fine sloping shoulders, good thick legs of mutton, and thick close wool of remarkable quality. His well-known rams included Little Guinea Peru, so called because Henry's younger brother Fred had sent ewes to his sire at 'one guinea per ewe'. Oh dear! The flock numbered up to 250 breeding ewes and was noted for the size and uniformity of

Southdown rams bred by Henry Webb of Streetly Hall, Cambridgeshire, 1888.
(*By kind permission, R. Langmead*)

Southdown ewe hoggets bred by Henry Webb, 1888. (*By kind permission, R. Langmead*)

frame and colour of the young females, which were regularly sold to France, Canada and the United States in particular. According to an article in *The Field* (August 1883), the French were the most eager customers, remembering the fine Jonas Webb Southdowns at the Paris International Exhibition in 1855.

The Streetly flock was dispersed in July 1889 (491 sheep) and the 247 lambs were sold the following year. Buyers included the Duke of Richmond, who had long been a Webb supporter, and the Prince of Wales. Top price for a pen of shearling ewes was paid on behalf of the MP, Mr J. J. Colman, a family name which is still well known among Southdown breeders today; and there were also many buyers from France, Germany, Canada, the USA and Australia. The Streetly flock was revived on a much smaller scale by Samuel Owen Webb, JP for Cambridgeshire, who was Henry's fourth son and who still owned Streetly Hall in the 1930s, having taken over the tenancy on his father's death and increasing it to 680 acres when he purchased the farm in 1912. Naturally he retained a good flock of Southdowns — and a herd of Dairy Shorthorns, Large Black pigs and some Suffolk Punches. He founded his first flock in 1890, using Babraham rams, and dispersed it in 1904 but started a new flock in 1926.

Meanwhile Henry's eldest son, Jonas M. Webb, became senior partner in John Thornton & Co., the London livestock auctioneers, and was a well-known judge of Shorthorns and Herefords as well as pigs and of course sheep: he always 'loved the Southdown best of all', and in 1901 the French Government created him an Officer du Mérite Agricole in recognition of his contribution to pedigree stock-breeding in France. He wrote many articles on the breed in the *Live Stock Journal*. Recalling his youth, he recorded:

> It was in the drought of 1868, that, as a little boy, I 'served my apprenticeship' cutting down boughs to feed a hungry flock of ewes each evening, at Streetly, where my father, Henry Webb, had established a flock from which all the leading exhibitors were purchasing their sires. It was there, he told me how lucky he was not to have a larger sheep to feed, as three Southdowns could live through the drought and be in better condition than two big sheep on the same ground. Since those days of childhood, however, I have lived to hear the late Mumford Sexton, when he had Suffolks to sell, describe how, in a drought, they could be seen, six at a time, racing to eat a daisy, so hardy were they! So there must be room for all breeds ... In 1878, I was at work at home. At

Michaelmas, we were sending rams to the United States. Samuel Sharpless ordered 'a straight back, brown face, one that has sheared at least 10 lb.' Mr Merrymen (Baltimore) also had one, and I sketched the face — not a speck of wool appears below the crown of the head or on the cheek below the line of the eye, 'muffle' headed Southdowns being my Father's aversion, as they were slow feeders, the wethers taking six weeks longer to fatten.

The second son, Henry, managed Lord Braybrooke's farm at Audley End and then Lord Howard de Walden's Welsh estate at Chirk. The third son, Frederick Noel, followed his grandfather's footsteps by managing for Mr C. R. W. Adeane at Babraham and later joined the Ministry of Agriculture, working on the livestock improvement and milk-recording schemes.

CHAPTER FOUR

Changing Fortunes for the Southdown

One of the strangest things in Sussex today is the disappearance of the sheep from the perfect pasturage of the Downland turf. Not more than a quarter of a century ago the Downs were dappled with white slowly moving flocks, and the quiet flat sound of the sharp bells could be heard far off on a still day. [Esther Meynell, *Sussex*, 1948]

John Ellman's improved Southdown sheep evolved on the stretches of the South Downs running eastwards from Shoreham. The maps of today's flocks show that the majority are still along this section of the Downs, including several major flocks, though there are also a few on the western Downs, on the coastal plain and the Isle of Wight to the south, and the Weald to the north. In addition the maps show how the breed is found in Kent and the Midlands in particular, and here and there in East Anglia, the West Country, Wales, Yorkshire and Scotland, though more than half the flocks are in southern England. A closer analysis suggests that about three in every four flocks are now on lowland holdings, in a wide range of situations, the rest being downland and other hill flocks.

A world map would show Southdowns in North and South America, New Zealand and Australia, and France and other European countries, while a map which included breeds heavily influenced by ancestral Southdowns would show an even greater spread. Yet in the

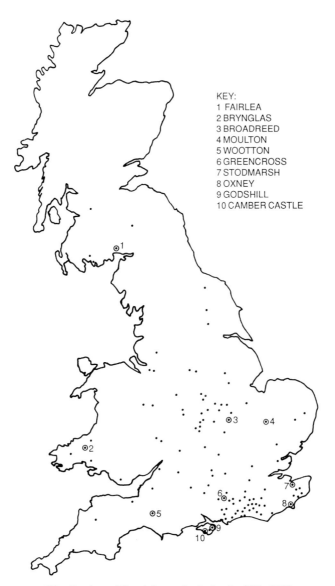

KEY:
1 FAIRLEA
2 BRYNGLAS
3 BROADREED
4 MOULTON
5 WOOTTON
6 GREENCROSS
7 STODMARSH
8 OXNEY
9 GODSHILL
10 CAMBER CASTLE

Distribution of Southdown flocks in the UK, 1990.

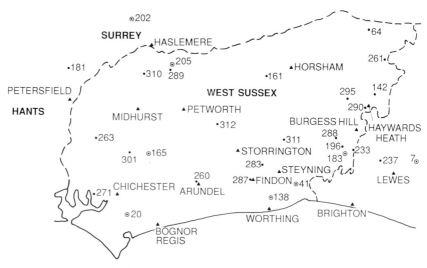

Key to map of Sussex flocks

Flock Number	Flock Prefix	Flock Number	Flock Prefix
7	RINGMER	161	BASHURST
20	MUNDHAM	165	EAST DEAN
41	CHAILEY	173	BARNHORN
64	GUNTON	181	MABBOTTS
101	COODEN	183	CHETWYND
113	SHERINGTON	189	WALDRON
138	STEEPDOWN	196	WESTMESTON
142	WALSTEAD	202	GREENCROSS (Surrey)

Southdown flocks in Sussex today.

How did it happen? How did the sheep which once blanketed the South Downs and were favoured by the dukes, earls and kings of the eighteenth and nineteenth centuries, fall to such low numbers so that most flocks today number a dozen or two breeding sheep and only a handful of top flocks reach three figures, and then in most cases only just?

After Ellman and Webb, the golden age of British agriculture continued until perhaps the 1870s, when the new worlds to which home country the Southdown has been classified as a rare breed by the Rare Breeds Survival Trust since 1987, when the number of pure breeding ewes fell to fewer than 1500. That is almost an insult to Ellman and his successors, though it could be that the Trust will prove vital to the breed's success in the next few years.

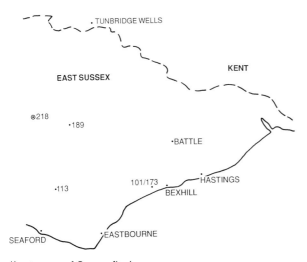

Key to map of Sussex flocks

Flock Number	Flock Prefix	Flock Number	Flock Prefix
205	DUNCTON	287	COOMBE LODGE
218	RIDINGS	288	OLDWAYS
233	STRAWBERRY DOWN	289	NORTHCHAPEL
237	UPPER MILL	290	CLEAVEWATER
260	ARUNDEL	295	(Mr Gradden's)
261	SULAMA	301	SINGLETON
263	MARDEN	310	BRIDGELANDS
271	CUTMILL	311	JESSUPS
283	CHANCTONBURY	312	HICKSTEAD

British livestock and expertise had been enthusiastically exported began to pour their own produce back into the lap of the motherland. These imports depressed British agriculture for more than half a century, sometimes severely, though the world continued to regard Britain as the cream producer of breeding stock. Meanwhile, the home market for fresh milk grew stronger and many sheep-and-arable farmers began to turn their attention to dairy cows, to the disadvantage of the sheep.

In 1899 more than 37 000 Southdown ewes were put to the ram. The majority of the flocks were in Sussex, especially around Lewes and Glynde in the east and Chichester in the west, though there were also large flocks in Hampshire, Essex, north Wales and southern Ireland at the turn of the century. Many of the flocks were on large estates, some with more than a thousand ewes each: the Prince of Wales put 409 ewes to the ram in 1899, a year in which there were among the Southdown Sheep Society's vice-presidents two dukes, four earls and five lesser peers. In 1911 registrations of Southdowns with the Society (formed twenty years earlier) reached a peak of 114 900 ewes in 372 flocks. In 1912 the breed was still being exported to New Zealand, France, Germany and Russia and also to more exotic countries such as India, Japan, Brazil, Jamaica and Portugal.

The First World War, however, almost halved the Southdown population at home and in 1920 registrations were only about 54 000, in 225 flocks. One of the major factors in this drop had been the general reduction in arable land area; sheep-folding on arable diminished accordingly — and the Southdown was essentially a folded arable sheep in spite of its grass-upland origins. It was also a small breed, with high quality wool and meat, but one result of the war was that quantity became more important than quality. In 1920 the alarm bells were

Judging shearling rams at the Chichester Show, 1916.

ringing: the Society's secretary forwarded to the Ministry of Agriculture and the National Farmers' Union figures showing the great reduction which had already taken place in the breeding of Southdowns and sought advice from Walter Langmead on the best method of framing a question (through the Duke of Richmond) in the House of Lords in the interests of the Southdown or, in fact, the Down breeds generally. 'It is clear,' wrote the secretary, W. J. Wickson, 'that a progressive decrease in the breeding of Down sheep must injuriously affect the production of both mutton and corn,' and indeed of wool. Langmead calculated a decline in the number of pedigree Southdown ewes by 32.5% from 1913 to 1918, 20% from 1918 to 1919, and 45% from 1913 to 1919.

However, Southdown exports to North America and New Zealand in particular continued in the 1920s and increased in the 1930s. The breed was geared to the export trade, which demanded small, blocky, short-legged and early-maturing stock to improve leggy, thin-bodied native breeds. (Among cattle, the Aberdeen-Angus was playing a similar role and its shape was developing along similar lines.) At home, for a while, the small, compact, meaty Southdown ram remained the

Southdown two-shear ram, 1930s. (*Sport and General*)

preferred sire for the family's traditional Sunday joint of roast lamb.
The breed was certainly small: Mrs Colman remembers that shearlings
on the Downs before 1940 were about the size of today's lambs at 8
months old. By 1938 only 28 339 ewes were put to the ram, and there
were only 153 flocks — a drop from 266 ten years earlier — though
several flocks still kept more than 500 ewes and the breed was still
sweeping the board at Smithfield. The Sandringham estate was still
putting 172 ewes to the ram that year and the aristocracy remained
well represented among the vice-presidents. The Southdown was
recognised as the quality lamb and was sought by the retail butchers
who were still essential in every village in the country. Most of the
Southdown flocks were kept for the production of prime lamb and the
sheep were folded, which required a great deal of labour but at that
time this was not such a significant element in the cost of production
and sheep were an essential part of the arable rotation on many
lowland farms.

The situation was changed by the traumas of the Second World
War. Huge areas were ploughed in an attempt to make Britain self-
sufficient quickly, but unfortunately there was no corresponding increase in the use of arable folding and the war took a considerable toll
on the Southdown flocks. Many flocks were reduced in number or cut
out altogether, so that by 1945 only 10 000 ewes were officially put to
the ram. More drastically for the Southdown, the breed's home downs
were hijacked for tank training and, on top of it all, quality (the breed's
trademark) was even more firmly rejected in favour of quantity: large
carcases were needed for maximum home meat production and farm
prices were paid per pound, regardless of quality. No doubt Bakewell
gave Ellman a knowing look and a chuckle from his grave.

Yet large numbers of Southdown rams and ewes were exported
during those war years: 257 females and 38 rams to the United States,
90 rams to New Zealand, substantial numbers to the Argentine and
Canada, and smaller numbers to Australia and Kenya. The 1950/51
editions of the Flock Book indicated a continuing interest from New
Zealand and the United States, and an increasing interest from France.
Despite a ban on exports to Australia, New Zealand and North
America in 1951, Southdowns still went abroad in good numbers,
purchased privately or through agricultural ministries in Brazil,
Romania, Poland, Hungary, Spain, Portugal, Tunisia, Italy, France,
Ireland and Kenya, and visiting international exhibitions in Moscow,

Paris and Tokyo. In due course, overseas bloodlines would come back to Britain: a couple of French rams were imported in 1970 for example, but of much greater influence on the British flock were New Zealand rams imported in the early 1960s and in 1979/80.

At home, after the Second World War, labour was scarce and wages were rising so that fewer flocks were folded. The Southdown's quality and small size were held against it for the mass market, though it managed to maintain its special qualities such as conformation, longevity, thriftiness, good wool and the ability of its lambs to survive. In post-war years the Ministry attempted to persuade sheep farmers to concentrate on smaller carcases but producers decided that such a policy was not profitable. It became more economic for commercial flocks to use more prolific crosses; the use of Scottish Halfbreds, Greyfaces, Welsh Halfbreds and, later, Mules became more widespread as transport became easier and cheaper. At first Southdowns competed with the other Down breeds as terminal sires on these crossbred ewes, but with guaranteed prices the larger lamb was found to be more profitable and the Suffolk, in particular, gradually assumed more importance. More recently larger carcases have found favour with the supermarkets and this could be another reason for the declining demand for the Southdown, which also has a reputation for becoming fat too readily for modern tastes.

Meanwhile the breed has improved immensely since the war, but today the demand is for good, long rams standing tall enough to cover big commercial ewes, and to some eyes the modern Southdown ram is losing the old-fashioned, chubby, meaty hindleg which is such an important feature of its top-quality conformation.

In spite of many breeders' attempts to breed what the market wants and what they can sell best (even when they might personally dislike the 'new' shape), the status of the Southdown continued to decline and in the 1970s the Rare Breeds Survival Trust began to keep an eye on the breed. In 1982 the Trust estimated that the population was at more than its critical level of 1500 breeding ewes, but numbers were still falling and, finally, in 1987 the threshold had been reached and it became officially a rare breed in spite of its continuing popularity abroad. The flock sizes had also reduced alarmingly: by 1985, 90% of the flocks had fewer than fifty breeding ewes and only one had more than a hundred.

The Southdown is still valued by serious breeders for quality meat

Champion Southdown ewes at the Royal Show, Newcastle, 1962. (*Sport and General*)

and wool. Although quantity has been the commercial yardstick for more than forty years now, there could well be a reversal of that trend in the more selective 1990s as long as the carcase is not too fat (which can be controlled by a combination of good breeding and good management). There are still some family butchers who value the quality of the Southdown and cater for those who appreciate flavour. It could be that there will be a swing away from bland supermarket meat so that when taste again becomes desirable the Southdown's popularity can be regained. In addition, the coming abolition of the variable premium in favour of a ewe premium could encourage commercial flock-owners to find more profit in a smaller lamb of higher quality. Whatever the future holds, the breed must be ready to take advantage of a swing back to quality and in the meantime continue to find special favour as a terminal sire for a 'bonus' lamb crop from ewe hoggs.

The Southdown's genes are widespread, both geographically and in other breeds at home and elsewhere, so that there is a good pool of genetic material ready to be tapped within the home breed and also by reinvigorating the home stock with overseas blood if desirable. Southdown breeders are at a crucial crossroads in the history of the breed, with the choice of keeping it as it is today in Britain in the hope that market demands will alter in its favour, selecting for larger (or smaller) types within the British flocks, or judiciously introducing fresh blood and new strains from, say, New Zealand, France, Australia or North America without losing the home breed's most valuable attributes such as early maturity, good flavour, excellent conformation and great docility.

There is always a risk that in trying to alter a breed to meet a contemporary market new or enhanced qualities are gained but old assets are lost along the way. Genetic manipulation, to any degree, is an art as much as a science and, like dominoes or playing-card houses, a gentle tweak here or a careless knock there can set off an unforeseen sequence of effects which might not be quite what was intended. Many breeds have already suffered in the race for quantity; they have lost their hardiness, their thriftiness, their fertility or their ease of parturition, perhaps, or they have ended up virtually indistinguishable from an existing breed which already does its own job better.

It is perfectly possible to increase carcase quantity without jeopardising quality if the breeding is carefully planned and all the consequences understood, but it is much easier to lose valuable genetic combinations than to recreate them. It is therefore to be hoped that Southdown breeders will value their heritage while they evaluate their future and that they will remember that any animal can only do its best if its husbandry, as well as its breeding, is appropriate to its needs and circumstances. Nor can any breed, even the best, meet its proper potential unless it is enthusiastically supported and jointly promoted by its breeders. The story of the Jacob breed is a marketing miracle which might be borne in mind.

The question now, with home numbers low, is whether or not the breed in its present form can take advantage of any market changes that might occur (or that might even be created or precipitated by those with the courage to promote their breed) and, if not, to what degree can or should it be 'modernised'? As the illustrations show (making due allowance for artistic licence in the old days) the breed has changed in shape and size over the centuries and will continue to do so. It is noticeable that Ellman aimed for a small, stocky type while Webb preferred a larger animal altogether. Within the home breed, there have always been larger and smaller strains and there is ample scope for selective breeding within British flocks today.

Recently some strains have become larger in the body and longer in the leg from careful outcrossing to the New Zealand rams imported first in the early 1960s, particularly a splendid Punchbowl and the influential Hieta ram. The New Zealand stock imported in 1979/80 were less like the traditional English Southdown. In his analysis of the Flock Book, Stephen Hall of Cambridge found that of the 68 rams which had sired ram lambs in the 1985/6 volume, all but 15 had some New Zealand or French blood, mostly only as ancestral traces but in 14 the New Zealand blood was 50–100%. The New Zealand type is generally bigger, with more daylight underneath and good eye-muscle, but there is a danger that some strains are losing the good hindquarter and, in becoming longer in the body, are becoming slack behind the shoulder and long in the neck. In a few there is a tendency towards the head becoming proportionately larger and coarser. which could possibly lead to an increase in lambing problems in the future, and also the fleece is becoming flatter, more open and too white. Ellman would have objected to the use of non-Southdown sires but he would have appreciated the value of reimporting Southdown blood from overseas in order to keep the breed a commercial one.

It *is* a commercial breed. Numbers can be deceptive in that the Southdown's role today is mainly as a terminal sire for prime lambs, so that its own numbers do not need to be high as long as the pure-breeding ewe flocks can supply the commercial demand for Southdown ram lambs. The total number of active commercial rams of all breeds in Britain is only about 30 000 each year.

There is today a certain amount of conflict among Southdown breeders about the direction in which they feel the breed might now be developed and this is generating some healthy discussion of views which will no doubt have a creative outcome. It would perhaps be to the benefit of the breed as a whole if there was to be a general consensus of opinion, but individual breeders must have the freedom to make their own choice in the matter. The views of different breeders are therefore quoted without prejudice in the hope of stimulating a continuing determination within the breed society to do what is best for the breed rather than for the individual.

Let any changes be tempered with caution and wisdom, lest the ancestral qualities so carefully developed over the last two centuries should be rashly, albeit unwittingly, destroyed or discarded. The breeders of the past are standing at your shoulder, watching, and among them is Ellman, who fully appreciated the great importance of publicity and promotion of his breed. Where today are those who helped him—the dukes, the Youngs, the Cokes and the Webbs?

That question was put to Hugh Clark, President of the Southdown Sheep Society in its centenary year, who has seen great changes in the past forty years. He remembers that, in his early years with the breed, the sheep rings and lines occupied by the Down breeds at the Royal Show would be thronged and with a good sprinkling of members of the nation's aristocracy, often accompanied by their agents, farm managers, head shepherds and under-shepherds and, bringing up the rear of these retinues, the lorry drivers (very few shepherds drove their own lorries then). Gradually, policies changed on the big estates and the old breed enthusiasts retired, died or simply faded away from the scene and at the same time the number of entries at the Royal dwindled alarmingly. Today, however, the sheep section is once again bursting at the seams, so that the numbers entered by each person must be restricted, but there is hardly a professional shepherd in sight. Now the preparation and exhibition of the sheep are carried out mainly by their owners, or sons and daughters, with the occasional help of young employees. The dukes and knights of the Southdown's heyday have left the arena and no longer vie with each other to produce the best with the invaluable aid of their remarkable shepherds. The Southdown's future depends not on the aristocracy but on working farm families, the true successors to the Webbs and the Ellmans.

CHAPTER FIVE

The Southdown Sheep Society

The Southdown was one of the earliest breeds to be methodically improved but it was not the first downland breed to have its own flock book or breed society. For example, the Shropshire's society was formed in 1882, the Suffolk's in 1886, and the Oxford Down's first flock book was published in 1889. The American Southdown Sheep-Breeders' Association was formed on 1 May 1882, and published its first *Southdown Record* or flock book in 1884.

It was not until July 1891 that Southdown flockmasters met on the show ground of the Royal Counties Society at Portsmouth and agreed to form a society or association because of their dissatisfaction with the breed and a desire to start a flock book for the registration of purebred sheep, partly prompted by the problems which were interfering with the export of sheep to America (because of the McKinley Bill). Their main aims were to secure greater purity in the breed and to maintain such purity. Their Southdown Sheep-Breeders' Association was incorporated in January 1892 and the first flock book was published in September of that year. The initial group of breeders included Mr Edwin Ellis (chairman and president) and Messrs F. N. Hobgen (auctioneer), Newton Clayton, Hugh Penfold, W. W. Chapman, W. Toop and E. M. Synge. The first official show and sales were held at Chichester on 26/27 June and 10/11 August, when the judges were C. O. Newman of Selhurst Park, Chichester, and John Heasman of Angmering.

However, several breeders did not approve of the new association and in February 1893 they formed their own Southdown Sheep Club, with Mr J. J. Colman, MP, as their president. For a while there was the slightly uncomfortable situation of two groups with broadly identical aims but in 1897, after the Club had published three volumes of its *Reports of Proceedings* and the Association had published five volumes of its flock book, they at last came together and were amalgamated as the Southdown Sheep Society.

The Society's principle objects were to encourage the breeding of Southdown sheep and to maintain the breed's purity. To this end it published an annual Flock Book containing flock returns for the year, pedigrees of registered rams and ewes, illustrations of typical sheep, prize records and other useful information. By 1929, more than a thousand flocks had been registered. The Society also undertook the official tattooing of registered-flock lambs intended to be retained for breeding purposes and by the 1930s this involved the tattooers in travelling 14 000 miles to almost every county in England and Wales.

The Society also issued export certificates and held flock competitions, which not only became popular but also produced marked improvements in the general standard of excellence of the breed throughout the country, and it further encouraged such improvements by offering handsome prizes at most of the major shows. In 1946 the Society was able to claim that, while it helped registered breeders to advertise and sell their sheep to the best advantage, it also safeguarded the purity of the breed and, above all, worked for the good of the breed itself.

By 1928 there were 310 registered members, increasing to 320 in 1929; prizes were offered for Southdowns at sixteen of the principal summer shows that year, while at the Royal Counties Show at Southampton the Southdowns easily outnumbered other breeds, with ninety-four entries. Sixty-eight were entered at the Royal Show at Harrogate — the largest entry in the sheep section — and there were 149 at the Sussex County Show at Brighton. High honours were secured at leading fatstock shows in Britain and the United States, and John Langmead's pen of three wether lambs were reserve for the Champion Plate and won the Gold Medal for the best pen of short-woolled sheep at the Smithfield Club Show, while other prizes were won in the carcase competition (purebred and crosses). Apart from major wins at Birmingham (His Majesty the King included), Norwich

Champion Southdown ewes at the Kent County Show, 1929, exhibited by Mr J. Pierpont Morgan. (*Sport and General*)

(the Earl of Derby), York (the Royal Flock at Sandringham again) and Edinburgh, the Southdown continued what had become a habit of winning the highest awards at the Chicago International Live Stock Exhibition, where several American agricultural colleges and universities took the prizes against stiff competition from other breeds and the British Society's own Challenge Cup was won for the third time in succession by Mr G. S. Belden of Mountain Farm, Bradstreet, Massachusetts.

Exports during 1929 went to the Argentine, Australia (where there was particularly keen interest), Brazil, Canada, France, Germany, Nigeria and Tasmania. However, four years later the export trade became dull, due to 'financial stringencies in the Dominions and other countries', though stock was exported to the Argentine, Australia, Brazil, Canada, Denmark, France, New Zealand and South Africa. Membership of the Society had fallen too: in 1933 the total number of members was 286, but show successes and high entries continued.

Members of the Southdown Sheep Society at an annual Field Day in Dumfries, Scotland, with their hosts Mr and Mrs Cyril Wise.

The third edition of *The Southdown Sheep* was published in 1936, this time as a hardback book drawn up by the Advertising Committee under the chairmanship of John Langmead (Walter Langmead was a committee member as well). There was a special subcommittee to deal with the advertising of Southdown mutton and lamb, in conjunction with approved butchers who were entitled to display the Society's official certificate and labels. The members stated:

> The greatest good for the majority of its flockmasters is ever the aim of the Council of the Society, and it has always to be borne in mind that *the breed is greater than the individual breeder*, and that while the Breed will endure for ever, flocks — individual flocks — must, in the course of time, be dispersed. The Society was formed by members of all classes to safeguard and promote the welfare of the Breed of Southdown Sheep, and that is, and ever will be, the motto of this Breed Society.

That view holds good today.

Official trade mark of the Society, tattooed in the left ear of each registered breeding Southdown sheep.

PRESIDENTS OF THE SOCIETY

1897–9	Earl Bathurst, CMG
1900	Lord Northbourne
1901	Mr Charles R. W. Adeane, CB
1902	Colonel Sir Nigel Kingscote, GCVO, KCB
1903	Mr Allan Cooper
1904	Admiral Hon. T. S. Brand
1905	Earl Cadogan, KG
1906	Mr Herbert Padwick, CBE
1907	The Duke of Richmond and Gordon, KG
1908	Sir Jeremiah Colman, Bt
1909	The Duke of Norfolk, KG
1910	Mr Alfred Heasman
1911	Lord Leconfield

1912	Mr Ernest Mathews, CVO
1913	The Marquis of Bristol, MVO
1914	Mr William Brown
1915	Viscount Hambleden
1916	Sir W. B. M. Bird
1917	Mr Harry Willett
1918	Sir Jeremiah Colman, Bt
1919	Revd C. H. Brocklebank
1920	The Duke of Richmond and Gordon, KG
1921	Mr R. S. Hicks
1922	Mr John Langmead
1923	Mr A. Miller-Hallett
1924	Revd C. H. Brocklebank
1925	Captain G. V. Baxendale
1926	The Duke of Northumberland, KG
1927	The Lady Ludlow, JP
1928	Lieutenant Colonel Sir W. A. Wayland, MP
1929	Lady Fitzgerald
1930	Mr Herbert Padwick, CBE
1931	The Duke of Richmond and Gordon, DSO, MVO
1932	Sir R. Sothern Holland, Bt
1933	Lady Loder
1934	Mr A. Miller-Hallett
1935	Hilda, Duchess of Richmond and Gordon
1936	Mr G. M. Scrutton
1937	Mr John Langmead
1938	Mr S. Owen Webb
1939	Sir Walter J. Halsey, Bt
1943	Mr Walter O. Stride
1946	Mr R. L. Hales
1947	Captain H. Tupper, MC
1948	Sir R. Sothern Holland, Bt
1949	Mr W. T. Forse
1950–1	Wing Commander R. G. Grant-Ferris, MP
1952	Captain Sir Thomas Halsey, BT, DSO, RN (ret'd)
1953	Mr John Craig, OBE
1954	Mr Percy Filkins
1955	Mr William Lee, JP
1957	Mr D. S. A. McDougall
1959	Wing Commander R. G. Grant-Ferris, MP
1960	Captain E. H. G. Trumper
1961	Mr R. Jopson, BSc

1962   Mr H. B. Paynter
1963   Lady Jean Philipps
1964   Mr B. D. Gough
1965   Mr H. T. Clark
1966   Mr S. B. Maxwell, BSc
1967   Mr R. M. Harris
1968   Mr Eric Pye
1969   The Marquess of Exeter
1970   Mr L. T. S. Hawkins
1971   Mr John Craig, OBE
1972   Mr C. H. Fowler
1973   The Rt Hon. Sir Robert Grant-Ferris, MP
1974   Mr G. C. Chapman
1975   Mr Frank H. Grantham
1976   Mr H. George Hughes
1977   Mr S. B. Maxwell, BSc
1978   Mr W. Maurice Chitty
1979   Mr Hugh T. Clark
1980   Mr David Craig
1981   Mr J. Mansel Hopkin
1982   Miss H. J. Paynter
1983   Mr Michael Shove, JP, FRICS, ASVA
1984   Mr G. H. Armstrong, MA, BSc
1985   Mr D. Humphrey
1986   Mr J. Randall
1987   Mrs S. Colman
1988   Mr F. H. Grantham
1989   Mr F. K. Mitchell, TD
1990   Mr Hugh T. Clark

SECRETARIES OF THE SOCIETY

There have been only six Secretaries of the Southdown Sheep Society: they tend to be loyal to their office for many years. The earliest (1891–98) was W. W. Chapman, a livestock agent and exporter, who was followed by W. J. Wickson of 12 Hanover Square, London. Little is now known of Wickson, who was succeeded in 1920 by Walter Osborne Stride, a partner in the old established firm of surveyors in Chichester at 63 East Street; a gentleman of the old school, Stride was Secretary for thirty years and was also President of the Society during the war

Mr Reg Noakes (Secretary until 1966 — second from left) with Mr Eric Pye, Major
Byers, Mr Leslie Burt and Mr Harold Paynter at the 1962 Field Day, Moulton.
(*John Salter Photography*)

years (1941–45). His son Dan C. Stride took over as Secretary for a
year (1950–51) and then handed the post to Reginald G. Noakes at 40
High Street, Maidstone, who rescued the Society from the doldrums of
the war. Southdowns on many large estates had been dispersed and the
membership gradually reduced but in these difficult times Noakes
worked hard for the breed with the help of his wife, Nellie. The
Centenary President, Mr Hugh T. Clark, was Noakes's first new
member.

The present Secretary (Clive Pritchard, who has held the post since
1967) remembers that Nellie used to lay out a large blanket on the grass
at shows and sales and, as Pritchard remarks, 'If you were invited to sit
on the blanket with her, you had arrived!' He reports on the
Secretary's duties today:

When I became Secretary in 1967, I received a three-page list of
instructions from the previous Secretary and the item that remains in my
memory is about the Findon Show and Sale: 'On the Saturday get up at

5 a.m., take a flask down to the Fairground and welcome all the members as they arrive and see the sheep are all bedded down in the marquee.' Times have changed since then — we do not have a marquee and only about two lots arrive before 8 a.m.

Twenty-two years is a long time. I knew nothing about Southdowns when I started and Mr Roland Harris, who was President, said that it was a good thing and I would learn. Now I am waiting for the Council to ask me to judge!

What does the Secretary do?

He keeps records of the Society, collects the annual subscription (which at £17 is very reasonable) and prepares the Flock Book for printing each year. He persuades members to register their Southdowns individually in the Flock Book if he can. He tries to get the Flock Book printed as cheaply as possible; at the moment it costs £900.

The four Council meetings have to be arranged and the agenda sent out. The Field Day and Annual General Meeting have to be arranged in August at a member's farm; all the members are notified and reminded to book their places.

Judges have to be selected by the Council for the shows at which there are Southdown classes:

The Royal Show
The South of England Show
The Kent Show
The Royal Welsh Show
The Royal Bath and West Show
The Findon Show and Sale
The Rare Breeds Survival Trust Show and Sale
The Royal Smithfield Club
The Flock Competition

Details of the Flock Competition and the Sam Maxwell Award are sent out and the results sent to all who enter.

The Secretary attends Breed Centres at the major shows where possible and his garage is full of the items needed. He makes all the arrangements for the Southdowns at the Findon Show and Sale in September, including a meal for all Council members (with the help of the ladies) and tea and coffee at all the major shows.

He also keeps the accounts of the Society, sends them to audit and keeps in close contact with the Treasurer. As well as all the above, he

Mr Clive Pritchard, present Secretary of the Southdown Sheep Society.

maintains contact with the National Sheep Association and deals with members' problems and requests for information and assistance.

Perhaps it should be a full-time job!

Clive Pritchard
Secretary, Southdown Sheep Society

CLIVE PRITCHARD
SOUTHDOWN LODGE
300 COPLE ROAD
CARDINGTON
BEDFORD   MK44 3SH
0234-838807

CHAPTER SIX

The Southdown Influence

Robert Bakewell's longwoolled Dishley Leicester and John Ellman's shortwoolled Southdown have been used for more than two centuries to create or improve the majority of British breeds and to influence many overseas sheep as well. The now dominant **Suffolk** originated very early in the 19th century from crossing Southdowns with the Norfolk Horn; the Suffolk was recognised as a breed in 1810 and was formally named in 1859 (it was also known as the Southdown Norfolk). The **Shropshire** was another early nineteenth-century breed produced by using Southdown rams on Cannock Chase, Longmynd, Morfe Common and other heath sheep: it was officially named in 1848 and a breed society established in 1882.

The **Hampshire Down** also originated early in the last century, this time from crosses of Southdowns with the Wiltshire Horn and Berkshire Knot; it was recognised as a breed in 1859, with its own breed society from 1889 and Flock Book from 1890, and it was then crossed with the Southdown to create the **Dorset Down** (originally known as the Improved Hampshire Down). Cotswold rams put on Hampshire Down (and Southdown) ewes produced the big **Oxford Down** recognised in 1851.

Many other breeds, in Britain and overseas, have been improved at some stage with the help of Southdown blood. For example, there is a possibility that Southdown rams were used during the eighteenth century to improve the **Cheviot** and it has also been suggested that the **Ryeland**, or Hereford, was developed into its modern type by the use of Leicester and Southdown rams. There have been many 'mixture' breeds, too, which betrayed their Southdown debt by giving themselves the prefix 'South': the South Suffolk (or Southfolk), for example, still thrives in New Zealand.

FRANCE

The Southdown reached its peak of popularity in France about 1963, when there were 605 000 head (not necessarily all registered) and it was the fifth most numerous breed in that country, representing nearly 7% of the sheep population. Today it is bred mainly near the heart of France: it shares its region with the Dishley-influenced Charollais and is found in cereal-growing areas where quick-growing, quality lamb is often finished indoors. This is typically the fate of Ile de France and Berrichon du Cher lambs and the early-maturing Southdown's main role, typically of English breeds in France, is as a terminal sire, though it is only in the last two decades that the French have really accepted the idea of producing crossbred lambs.

The first Southdowns came to France in 1827 when a few were imported on an experimental basis by Le Comte de Bouille, of Villars, who, dissatisfied with local sheep, wanted a hardy, adaptable and easily lambed breed which would withstand the frequent temperature and humidity variations in the local climate. The Exposition Universelle de Paris in 1855 created considerable interest in the breed, especially after Webb's gift of his ram to the Emperor, and in the same year fifteen expensive in-lamb ewes from Jonas Webb's Babraham flock were added to de Bouille's collection, with another fifty-five Webb ewes following in 1857 and a Webb ram purchased at the Chelmsford Show in 1856.

In 1865 a flock of 100 ewes and three rams (one of which had won first prize at Norwich in 1864) formed the basis of the La Manderie flock of M. Nouette-Delorme, who also bought a ram from the dispersal of Henry Webb's flock. In 1884 Baron Mallet started a flock by purchasing some of Lord Walsingham's Southdowns and in 1896 the Baron made a gift of a dozen young ewes and a ram to M. Emile Petit of Orsigny. The latter bought Baron Mallet's entire flock in 1901 and then sold it in 1919 to Baron Henri de Rothschild, of Les Vaux de Cernay, who practised the latest scientific and experimental methods of flock husbandry and selective breeding at his National Centre of Zootechnical Experimentation. The flock was dispersed in 1934.

These original flocks had been dispersed by the 1930s. Some of the Villars flock contributed to the La Chasnay of M. R. Eustache, who imported nine new rams and ram lambs and twenty ewes and ewe lambs between 1904 and 1913. The La Manderie flock was purchased by M. Edmund Fouret of La Norville, who bought the well-known ram Hopeful at the dispersal of Mr C. R. W. Adeane's Babraham flock in 1913 and still had one of France's leading flocks before the Second World War. During the interwar years Southdowns were being exported to France in ever-increasing numbers and were rapidly becoming popular: in 1932 there were 196 000 French Southdowns. Unfortunately the French Southdown Society's records were destroyed during the German occupation but by 1947 there were 300 000 of the breed. Since the 1960s peak the breed has regressed and by 1983 there were 175 000 ewes, mainly in Poitou-Charentes, Limousin and Aquitaine. The trend in recent years has been for sires able to produce larger, heavier carcases (18–20 kg rather than 15–16 kg) with no fat, and in most regions the French Southdown is a heavier and taller type than the English.

In 1970 Sam Maxwell, manager of the Eartham flock in Sussex, accompanied Roland Harris to France and they selected five rams on behalf of the Southdown Sheep Society. Only two passed the test and were purchased, neither of them outstanding specimens and one in particular was very short. However, Mrs Sheila Colman has attended recent Paris shows and in 1990, when only rams were shown because of lack of space, she noted that the standards were improving and the number of entries increasing; the top prizes went to the bigger, longer rams which had good bodies and back ends but were rather long in the head and had large ears. The smaller, more traditional rams liked by some British judges, and with good heads as well as back ends, were not popular with the French judges.

The Southdown influence on other French breeds has been strongest on the exceptionally hardy **Vendéen**, an ancient breed with a history stretching back to the tenth century and influenced by English imports even in the twelfth century. The Vendéen's main influence was in the mid-nineteenth by the first major importation of Southdowns to

France and it still looks like a dark-faced Southdown today, though rather coarser and more open-coated. The Vendéen has the Southdown's early maturity and the bonus of improved prolificacy as the result of selective breeding and a policy of including only multiple-litter lambs in the Flock Book established in 1967.

Nineteenth-century Southdown breeding is also obvious in the colour and head shape of the **Avranchin**. Other French breeds with Southdown blood include the **Bizet** of the Massif Central, which arose from the Caussenard crossed with Southdown and Dishley Leicester in the nineteenth century; the **Cotentin**, originally Southdown on local Roussin de la Hague in the early nineteenth century; and the **Lacaune**, southern France's main Roquefort breed, which had repeated infusions of Southdown and Merino blood before 1870. Several other French breeds used Southdown and Dishley Leicester rams for improvement in the nineteenth century.

NEW ZEALAND

Sheep were brought to New Zealand in the 1830s, initially to supply settlers and traders with fresh mutton. Genuine sheep farmers began to establish themselves in the following decade and it seems that the first Southdowns sailed to New Zealand on the *Timandra*, with ten ewes and two rams landing at Taranaki in February 1842, imported by a Mr Devenish. No one knows what happened to them or their descendants. The most decisive importation, which established the breed in New Zealand, was of 101 ewes and three rams descended from Jonas Webb stock and sold to the Deans Estate Trustees in Riccarton by Henry Matson of Christchurch in 1864 — a flock which was still in existence a century later. Then came the miracle of refrigeration, which was to change the whole future of the country's sheep-farming industry. The first shipload of frozen New Zealand sheep meat reached London on 24 May 1882, ninety-eight days after setting out from Port Chalmers.

The first flock to be registered in New Zealand's Flock Book was the Kirkstyle, which still exists today. However, only 950 ewes, in five flocks, were registered in that first British breeds' Flock Book, published by the New Zealand Sheep Breeders' Association in 1895, and there were only 25 members by 1904. It was not until 1920 that the Southdown really began to find its feet.

Between 1900 and 1920 there had been a comfortable increase of 2000 Southdowns annually. The English market was beginning to demand small, plump lamb carcarses produced by Southdown rams on larger ewes and between 1920 and 1930 the Southdown population suddenly increased by 18 000 a year, largely because of the demands for lightweight early-maturing carcases for export at premium prices. By 1926 the Southdown's popularity was growing so fast that the Southdown Sheep Society of New Zealand was formed, issuing its first Flock Book in 1927, when there were 590 members.

New Zealand's finest export lamb came from the best Southdown rams put to good Romney ewes on good grass (though many still preferred pure Southdown carcases) and it was this cross, or the Southdown on Leicester ewes, that formed the basis of the famous Canterbury frozen lamb trade. It produced what was described as a short, nuggety carcase which fetched the top prices on the London Market, and the cross also produced the type of lightweight mutton carcase which was in great demand at the time. Just before the Second World War, a New Zealand correspondent writing in *Farmer and Stockbreeder* said that

> the British consumer's cry for the small joint of good quality meat has not fallen upon deaf ears so far as the New Zealand producers are concerned; and it was in their stern realisation that greater attention to quality was imperative, if the Smithfield market was to be retained, that led to the wholesale adoption of the Southdown. When mated with the long-wool sheep of British breeds — particularly the Romney — the Southdown sire excels.

The combination of carcase quality and quick finishing was a winner, especially as the Southdown was well able to stand diminished food supplies and to respond again to good treatment. On North Island in the 1940s the sheep were on grass all year round, in flocks ranging from about 50 to 400; in the South Island they were virtually confined to Canterbury, where the low rainfall and less succulent feed were much more suitable than in the North, where they tended to suffer from foot rot and too much watery food in wet seasons but became too fat in dry seasons on good land. The Canterbury crossbred lambs were slaughtered for export at 4 to 6 months old, at dressed weights of 32 to 38 pounds, but local consumers were less fortunate. The point was made that 'the New Zealand butcher thinks more of quantity than quality, and consequently buys the heavier mutton and lamb. The average city consumer knows very little of the difference in quality of the mutton of the various breeds, and though he may grumble at what his butcher supplies, he has not the knowledge to demand anything better.' Holding over lambs for increased weight could ruin an otherwise first class early maturing carcase by allowing the development of unwanted, wasted fat.

The Second World War, of course, put a bit of a brake on the expansion of the Southdown in New Zealand because quantity became more important than quality, though in the 1940s they were still increasing at the rate of 14000 a year. Then the rate suddenly accelerated to 30000 a year between 1952 and 1957, and to 36000 a year from 1957 to 1962. In 1990 there were only 17 flocks in the country and 9000 sheep; in the 1960s there were more than 1700 flocks and nearly a million Southdown sheep, including more than 260000 registered with the Society, and the Southdown ram-breeding flocks were distributed all over the country to satisfy the demand for rams from export-lamb farms. In forty years the number of registered flocks increased seven-fold and the population of registered sheep twelve-fold.

Some of the major New Zealand breeders were James Knight (the Feilding flock), who preferred the traditional small English type and continually introduced fresh breeding stock from the home country, and Mr Roland Perry, OBE, who imported John Langmead's ram Ford Christian from Sussex and used him to linebreed a distinctive type of his own. The climate of New Zealand seemed to encourage a natural increase in the breed's size and between 1950 and 1970 the New Zealand Southdown dramatically changed in appearance. The 1950 ram was 2.2 times the length of its average depth; the 1960 ram 2.4 times and the 1970 ram 2.8 times, and this extra length, which was in the loin, was deemed to be an important factor in avoiding an undesirably overfat condition which often resulted from grazing the very palatable grasses of New Zealand's well-dressed land. The breed had also been lifted off the ground and had lost its rather thick shoulder.

The major influence on the New Zealand breed in this century is probably that of the Punchbowl Stud of Maheno, founded in 1915 by Mr Henry J. Andrew; it was the country's leading flock until its dispersal in 1977/78. Mr Andrew's first 30 ewes were of imported English blood and came from the flock of his grandfather, Mr H.

Pannet of Springston, Canterbury — the sixth in the Flock Book and founded in 1876. Andrew also bought ewes from Mr J. B. Reid and his early imported rams came from the Royal flock at Sandringham, the Luton Hoo flock, the Gatton Park Stud and other top English studs. Punchbowl sheep began to win many prizes and continued to do so until Mr Andrew retired from showing in 1948, since when sheep with Punchbowl blood have carried on the tradition by winning numerous Royal Show championships and major prizes. Punchbowl sheep also claimed record-breaking prices at auction and were widely exported, finding their way to the United States, Canada, Brazil, Tasmania, Japan, England and, with particular effect, Australia.

By the mid 1970s there were about a thousand Southdown stud breeders in New Zealand, producing the sires for crossing with Romney, Corriedale and other breeds for the country's famous Down

New Zealand 'Punchbowl' ram, imported by the Society in 1965.
(*Farmer and Stockbroker Photography*)

lamb, and homebred Southdowns were even being exported to Kashmir for crossing with native sheep to improve their wool quality.

There were still 532 flocks in 1976, when the move to larger, crossing sires had caused a decline in the Southdown's popularity, and the New Zealand breed society had already taken steps to increase the size and particularly the length of the Southdown by selective breeding. It was sheep of this big, strong type which caught the eye of Mr and Mrs Philip Whitcombe when they visited New Zealand in 1979 with a brief from the Southdown Sheep Society in Britain to bring a few good rams and ewes back with them in order to give more strength to the British breed. The Whitcombes' Greencross flock in Surrey is based entirely on New Zealand stock.

Today, however, the number of active Southdown breeders in New Zealand has declined sharply, though the Gatton Park flock of David Wyllie of Ashburton (which was named after Colman's famous English flock), the Merrydowns (Graham Robertson of Gore) and the Merryvale (Collin and P. J. Robertson of Gore) and the Clifton Downs (William J. and Christopher Medlicott) remain well known. The Whitegate flock was dispersed by John Ferguson in 1985 but most good pedigrees have Whitegate blood. The noted Tahrua flock of Mr Macauley has been bought by a new breeder, Mr H. T. Brenssell of Heriot (in the Gore area), who owns the Fernvale flock and also purchased Mr Potter's Ohio flock.

AUSTRALIA

Southdowns came to Australia with early colonists. In 1788 the Cressy Company founded the breed in Tasmania and the Revd Samuel Marsden (the 'flogging parson'), who arrived in the colony of New South Wales as the settlement's second chaplain in 1793, imported not only Christianity but also Southdowns, which were crossed with Indian breeds brought in shortly after the settlement was established in 1788.

It was not until 1898 that reliable records were at last established, when the Royal Agricultural Society of Victoria issued the first Flock Book for British sheep breeds; the two registered flocks that year were that of Mr Alexander Cameron of Cranbourne (who in 1895 had purchased Sir Edward Mitchell's Barfold flock, bred from imported English stock) and that of Mr Frederick Peppin of Fernbrook Loch, one of the brothers who had established the famous Wanganella strain of Merinos in 1861. Peppin established his Southdown flock in 1884 by purchasing from Mrs Woodhouse of Campbelltown, New South Wales, ten ewes and a ram (the latter originally imported from Colonel Kingscote of Gloucestershire). In 1889 he added two Summersbury ewes from Mr Edwin Ellis in Surrey and a ram by Merston, the famous sire bred by Lord Walsingham. Later, Peppin's son Guy would establish a Southdown stud at Murchison. In the Flock Book's second volume, published in 1902, there were two more Southdown flocks in Victoria (those of Mr Samuel King of Scotts Creek and Mr Alfred Blake of Monomeith); by the mid 1930s there were more than 200, and in 1966 the number of flocks had doubled.

In the early years the Australian sheep industry was interested only in wool, and the Merino had been ubiquitous since its introduction from the Cape in 1797. However, by about 1880 it was realised that sheep could also produce meat. Countries like New Zealand and Argentina, realising that their wool was inferior to that of Australia, had already made huge strides in improving lamb and mutton production and began to export their sheep meat to Britain. Some 80% of Australia's hundred million sheep were Merinos, not at all suited to the demands of Smithfield, but crossbreeding programmes were gradually developed and it was found, over about fifty years, that the Southdown ram on the first-cross longwool Merino ewe (from Lincoln, Romey, Border or Leicester rams) gave the depth and breadth in flesh in the leg and loin that would fetch the best prices in London. By the 1930s the 'Down Cross' was so successful that Southdown rams always auctioned at higher prices than other British breeds, though the very early maturity and fecundity of the Dorset Horn ran it a close second. The most tireless Southdown user of the period was Mr Archie Browning of Riverslea, Yarrawonga, Victoria, who made a close study of meat production for many years with the specific aim of supplying Smithfield, and found that Southdown lambs were heavier at an earlier age than other breeds. His successes in that market generated considerable enthusiasm in Australia for the Southdown ram and just before the Second World War that enthusiasm was running very high: Southdown breeders were full of optimism for their breed's future.

However, the Southdown was being bred to suit the demand for small, meaty carcases on the domestic and UK markets, and the larger Poll Dorset began to replace the Southdown in Australia. Although there were more than 400 flocks in 1966, they were experiencing the same increasing preference for bigger crossing sires as New Zealand. The combination of size and the embargo on the importation of sheep into Australia put the Southdown at a considerable disadvantage after the establishment of the European Economic Community and the new demand for leaner, larger, meatier carcases on the domestic and overseas markets. In 1973 the government lifted its ban on imports and breeders began to bring in some of the best strains from New Zealand. There has since been a dramatic improvement as the longer-bodied New Zealand rams (especially Punchbowl and Braemore stock) began to have a strong influence on the Australian type, making it much larger, longer and taller and putting it back into competition with the Poll Dorset.

The imports of rams and ewes from New Zealand and the breeders who have imported them are too numerous to mention but the result is that Southdowns have again found their place in the market. Sales of flock rams are improving every year as commercial breeders realise that the modern Australian Southdown used as a terminal sire over most longwool breeds and their crosses gives higher returns per hectare, whilst still retaining the Southdown characteristics of ease of lambing, hardiness and high quality meat. The 1989–90 prime lamb selling season saw an exceptionally strong demand for Southdown-sired lambs by meat wholesalers and retailers for both domestic use and export. The Royal Melbourne Show Society, which recently instituted a policy of featuring a breed of sheep at its Annual Royal Show, selected the Southdown for the 1989 Royal — the first British breed to be featured — and there were 176 entries from nineteen exhibitors. Lambs sired by Southdown rams are winning numerous carcase competitions throughout Australia under all systems of judging and competing against all breeds.

Today more than half of Australia's Southdown studs are in Victoria and there are about 137 registered flocks, including one of 660 ewes. The oldest studs still in existence are the Cambridge in Tasmania, founded in 1870 from the original Cressy flock, and the Kirkdale Lodge, established in 1884 and owned by Mr T. Hogarth. Most of the leading breeders are now using New Zealand blood.

UNITED STATES OF AMERICA

The Southdown has been strong in the United States since the last century and is now promoted by its thriving and very active breed society as not only the most efficient and economical but also a 'kinder and gentler breed' ideally suited to junior livestock exhibitors — the Southdown breeders of the future. Support for youth programmes is rightly considered of great importance and the American Southdown Breeders' Association, which celebrated its centenary in 1982, also stresses the need to preserve the breed's traditional natural muscling

USA Champion ewe, bred by Mr Gale Cole of Illinois, at the International Southdown Show, Louisville, Kentucky, 1989.
(*By kind permission, the American Southdown Breeders' Association*)

qualities and maintain the breed's integrity while increasing productivity and growth. After a record-breaking 11 379 new registrations in 1959, numbers fell to a low point in 1974 but are now climbing again to healthy levels. At present, as in the past, Southdowns are raised predominantly in small family flocks but there is a marked difference between the Southdown of fifty years ago and the American type today, not only in increased size but also in colour and wool covering, and the recent practice of presenting the sheep 'slick-shorn' at shows and sales serves to show off the breed's excellent conformation.

It is possible that sheep from the South Downs were among those brough to Viriginia and Massachusetts during the seventeenth century, but the first definite evidence of Southdowns in the US comes from a government document referring to an advertisement in a Philadelphia paper at the very end of the eighteenth century, announcing the arrival of some pure Southdowns but with no indication of their source in England. In 1803 it seems that a Dr Rose began producing wool from his small pure Southdown flock in Seneca County, New York, but in 1813 he crossed them with Merinos at a time when the Merino was the most fashionable breed in the country.

From 1824 to 1829 there is documentary evidence that some Ellman Southdowns were imported and later some Webb stock came into Pennsylvania, New York and Illinois. The first volume of the *American Southdown Record* noted that from 1780 to 1810 John Ellman was striving for a 'small and good' type but that a quarter of a century later Jonas Webb's type was 'large and good' — a change mirrored much later when the breed in some countries, including the United States, became very small in the 1940s but is decidedly larger today.

The early imports went mainly to New York, Pennsylvania, Ohio and Kentucky — and indeed the Blue Grass State provided such an excellent substitute for the sweet grazing of England's South Downs that the breed has always been popular here where it soon developed into a larger, longer-legged sheep. The importations continued during the nineteenth century from England's best flocks. The Southdown's popularity increased until the outbreak of the Civil War in 1861, which put a stop to imports and disrupted many established flocks. 1861 was also the year of the dispersal in England of the Babraham flock, from which John Taylor founded his own pure flock of Southdowns at Holmdale, New Jersey.

The breed was able to build up again after the Civil War and by

1920 there were more than 8000 in the country, including a prize-winning flock of Sussex blood which grazed New York's Central Park from 1865 to 1934. By 1929 Southdowns had spread through 38 States and by 1932 Kentucky headed the league with 100 active members of the American Southdown Breeders' Association, while Tennessee, West Virginia and Ohio also boasted good numbers. In 1930 there were nearly 13 000 and it was the country's sixth most common breed. In that year the Southdown Sheep Society in England encouraged further interest by presenting a Perpetual Cup for the best flock of registered Southdowns belonging to a member of the ASBA who exhibited at the International in Chicago. By the mid 1930s the breed's popularity was growing steadily: there was a tremendous demand for Southdown rams to breed commercial ewes, supplying the American east coast markets, and it had more influence on mutton improvement than any other breed. The Americans were still importing many of their Southdowns from the home country before the Second World War, especially Langmead rams from the Ford flock.

In 1893 English-bred Southdowns had taken nearly all the prizes at the Chicago World Fair and in the first 35 years of the twentieth century, purebred Southdown wethers were awarded the Grand Championship at Chicago's huge International Live Stock Exposition nineteen times, not to mention the breed's countless other successes in carcase competitions. Between 1929 and 1939, Southdowns won practically every prize at Chicago and the breed's popularity continued after the war. By the mid 1940s the Southdown sire was still America's outstanding favourite for superior meat production and the wethers were still winning at Chicago. Crossbred Dorset and Merino lambs from Southdown rams were particularly popular for Christmas or 'hot house' lamb.

Southdowns continued to dominate Chicago's champion wether, carcase and 'carload' classes, winning the single lamb Grand Championship there 39 times between 1910 and 1969. The final Chicago International was held in 1975, the year in which the first sheep show was held at the North American International Livestock Exposition at Louisville, Kentucky, and there has been a National Southdown Show at Louisville every year since 1978.

Mrs Sheila Colman cast a British eye over the American sheep at the 1990 show and comments that the practice of showing them slick-shorn ensures that the outline seen is meat, not trimmed wool. Most of the

USA Champion Flock exhibited at the Chicago International during the 1930s.

rams were long on the leg, with long necks and not deep-bodied, showing the New Zealand influence, while the ewes, to her eye, were of better quality with deeper bodies and shorter in the leg but with longer faces and larger ears than traditionally preferred in the UK. She was particularly impressed by the large number of breeders exhibiting Southdowns, the large numbers in each class, and also by the fact that all the sheep were shown without halters, restrained only by a hand behind the head and under the chin: they looked more alert, walked well and very rarely escaped from their handlers.

The American Sheep Breeders' Association (ASBA) offers four perpetual challenge cups for the breed (Champion Ram, Ewe, Pair of Ram Lambs, and Flock). The Association was first incorporated in 1882 and since then only six people have held the position of Secretary. One of them was Dr W. L. Henning, who was fifty years in the post from 1924 and who shook the association back into shape after it had become virtually bankrupt in 1922.

In the early years ASBA published 21 hardback volumes of its *American Southdown Record*, which was much more than a flock book: it also contained articles, photographs and show results. The first volume was published in 1884 but the logistics of publication became overwhelming: the youngest sheep listed in Volume 21, for example, was already 10 years old and virtually all the sheep catalogued in that volume were already dead by the time it was actually published in 1938. The first animal registered by the association had been a ram born before 1854 (so that it pre-dated the publication of the first flock book by more than 30 years), imported from England by Jonathan Thorne of New York and sold to L. Tarlton of Lexington, Kentucky. By the mid 1990s it is anticipated that the Association will have registered a grand total of half a million pure Southdowns since 1882.

The President of the ASBA, Gale R. Tempel of Wiley, Colorado, has contributed the following inspiring report:

Southdowns in America today

The American Southdown Breeders' Association is the oldest sheep breed association in the United States. It was incorporated under the laws of the State of Illinois on June 23 1882, and celebrated its Centennial in 1982. During the ensuing 108 years the breed and the Association have had their ups and downs, but 1990 finds us in a very comfortable position.

After the Second World War the market for Southdowns, and lamb in general, diminished: some speculate that this was the result of the American GI's distaste for the poorly prepared mutton that was the staple of the military K-rations. Demand was weak into the 1950s and by then the trend for purebred animals in the US was to short, heavy individuals who carried a large amount of fat. As the 1960s progressed, the animal industry began to look for a larger, taller animal but our gene pool lacked the basic stock to respond to this challenge. However, with the importation of purebred rams from New Zealand in the mid 1960s (particularly Punchbowl stock from Henry Andrews of Springston, Canterbury) the American Southdown began to grow and today it is a medium-sized animal which does an excellent job of converting roughage into muscling.

The present popularity of the Southdown in the United States is evidenced by increased registrations, transfers and new members in recent years. In spite of the relatively small percentage of American purebred sheep that are Southdowns, the breed ranks first or second in numbers at most major sheep expositions and sales across the United States. In 1989 our Association registered 5830 Southdowns but our major show had 249 individual entries and 15 flocks were shown in the Flock Class.

The American Southdown breeder is a very aggressive promoter and vocal enthusiast. Despite a limited budget, the Association is a leader among American sheep breed organizations in new and innovative promotional materials, projects and commitment to our breed. For example, Southdowns are the first breed to require 'slick shearing' at our National Shows and Sales. This practice, involving the complete shearing of the animals within five days of a show, is very popular with breeders, buyers and spectators alike. We feel the technique has boosted our breed's credibility and quality, as the animal must stand entirely on its own attributes and not the skills of an expert, professional showman.

Much of the success of the Southdown breed — in fact, a large proportion of the sales of all purebred sheep in the United States — depends on our youth organizations, 4-H and FFA (Future Farmers of America). Market lamb competition is particularly keen in the south-western states of Texas and Oklahoma. Top lambs will bring premiums in the thousands of dollars from local business people who support the youth programs. The breeding aspect of the sheep industry is equally popular and is often tied into our school systems. In most rural and many suburban communities, FFA is an extracurricular school activity. Our major shows have an open show and junior division, limited to exhibitors under 21 years of age.

The Southdown easily adapts to these youth programmes because of its gentle nature, lower initial investment, low maintenance cost and medium size. The American Southdown Breeders' Association actively promotes Southdown youth activities and supports a Junior Southdown Association. The young people of a nation are not only its future but also the future of an organization and breed such as ours.

The Association's aggressive promotion of the Southdown in the United States, coupled with the superior animal we have developed, makes the Southdown the breed to match in the US.

CANADA

The first pure Southdowns reached Canada in 1845. Initially the breed's strongholds were in Ontario and Quebec near the large cities where people appreciated and paid for quality lamb. Soon they became scattered right across the country in a wide range of climates and environments and numerous flocks were established to provide stud rams which, crossed on larger stock ewes, produced very deep, compact carcases of excellent growth and quality. In the 1940s at least 75% of the prizes at the Royal Agricultural Winter Fair in Toronto were won by Southdowns and their crosses and the future was looking very bright indeed, as it was said at the time, 'especially when the world gets back to a quality basis for its mutton and lamb'. In Canada, as elsewhere, the Southdown has suffered at the slide into a preference for quantity rather than quality, and in 1984 only 265 new registrations were entered, compared with more than 5000 Suffolks and 2200 Dorset Downs, though even then the Southdown held sixth place in the registrations table.

Major Canadian breeders included John Jackson & Sons and Mr T. C. Douglass, both in Ontario in the late nineteenth century, Colonel Robert McEwen & Sons in the 1920s and 1930s, and C. J. and W. G. Brodie in the 1930s and 1940s, each in turn dominating the Chicago championships and contributing to the development of the breed in the United States. Perhaps the most interesting of its time was the Don Head flock near Richmond Hill, Ontario, founded in 1928 with British stock imported by John D. Patterson who particularly favoured the Sandringham and Luton Hoo sheep. On his sudden death in 1940 the flock was dispersed to breeders in Ohio but the farm at Don Head was eventually bought by the Dutch immigrant W. Redelmeier in 1939 and he established a new Southdown flock, based on imports and boosted in 1948 when he repurchased the entire flock of Earl Jenkins, one of the Ohio breeders who had bought at the original Don Head dispersal. Thereafter the new Don Head breeding flock supplied top rams and ewes throughout the United States and Canada, until it was dispersed in 1958.

ASIA AND AFRICA

Several countries have made trial imports of Southdowns since the Second World War, none of which has been very successful. In 1954 two rams were imported by the Government of Bombay for trials at their experimental farm at Poona, where they were crossed with

Merinos. The wool from the first fleeces of these two rams was woven into a shawl and presented to the Prime Minister of Bombay, Mr Morarji Desai, but unfortunately the director of the farm (who had been responsible for the importation) was moved to a central government post in Delhi and nothing more was heard of the project.

In 1964 the Japanese asked for a few Southdown, Romney Marsh, Ryeland and Border Leicester sheep for the International Livestock Show at Chiba, near Tokyo. However, the Japanese sheep industry has not made much headway, as it is more economic to import lamb from Australia and New Zealand for this densely populated country.

When Kenya was still a British colony there were several importations of Southdown sheep but the sheep industry has not really flourished since Kenya's independence.

CHAPTER SEVEN

Some Famous British Flocks and Breeders

Although Ellman, Coke and Webb were so influential in establishing the Southdown as a breed, there were several other famous breeders over the years, of course, and many of the earlier ones would have been well acquainted with Ellman.

In 1814 Southdowns found themselves far from Sussex in a very different environment when Hugh Watson of **Keillor** (near Perth), already well known as the great improver of polled Angus cattle, bought some ewes at Lord Lynedoch's dispersal sale and gradually worked up a flock of 1000 ewes kept at altitudes of 500 to 1200 feet above sea-level, where apparently they proved very profitable. He liked Southdowns because they were easy to control, they could withstand severe winter storms and pick up again in spring more quickly than any other short-woolled breed, they were always success-fully fattened, and they could cover more ground for their food than any other type of sheep without losing their growth. He explained their hardiness in such conditions: 'The wool of the Southdown is so closely matted on their backs and about the head and neck as to be almost impervious to rain or snow, hence as soon as a storm ceased they appeared to be dry and comfortable and not the least disordered.'

The Keillor flock remained hardy and healthy for the twenty-five years of its existence and the ewes were noticeably easy to manage at lambing and were good mothers, giving ample milk on moderate keep

Three Southdown wethers, owned by His Grace the Duke of Richmond and Gordon. Champions at the Royal Smithfield Show, 1916. (*By kind permission, the Trustees of the Goodwood Collection*)

and happy to take the ram again almost as soon as the lambs were weaned. There are still some important Southdown flocks in Scotland today.

One of the oldest and longest-standing flocks was that of the Duke of Richmond at **Goodwood**, which was probably established before 1778 and continued a long way into the present century. The Royal Family, too, had supported Southdowns since King George III had met Ellman in the 1790s and in 1866 the Prince of Wales (later Edward VII) founded the **Sandringham** flock based on stock from Goodwood and others, including Webb animals. This royal flock was still exhibited regularly and successfully at major shows before the Second World War and some of the stock came originally from Lord Walsingham's **Merton** flock, which from 1851 to 1870 won 280 prizes, eighty-six medals and twenty-seven cups at leading shows in Britain, France and Pomerania. The flock was dispersed in 1885.

The Duke of Bedford's **Woburn** flock was almost as old as the Goodwood and was winning gold medals at Smithfield in the 1830s.

Three shearling rams belonging to His Majesty King George V. Champions at the Royal Show in the 1930s.

Francis Duke of Bedford's special gold medal was awarded to an even more prolific prize-winner, Mr Stephen Grantham's **Stoneham** flock near Lewes; Grantham started breeding Southdowns in 1810 and accumulated numerous Smithfield awards over thirty years. Towards the end of his 'reign', Mr W. Rigden of **Hove** began to sweep the board at the Royal and the Bath & West; his flock was founded on Babraham stock and he dispersed his 540 'splendid movers' in 1883, when Sandringham paid the top prices.

Five years later the century-old **Selsey** flock was dispersed by Mr Hugh Penfold; it had been brought to Selsey from Wiggonholt (near Pulborough) in 1836 and included rams from Thomas Ellman, Henry Webb and Goodwood. With Newton Clayton, Penfold was also part-owner of the **Pagham Habour** company flock, established in 1879, whose short-legged, deep-bodied sheep were noted for their hardiness and the density of their wool. In the first years of the new century nearly 1000 Pagham Harbour ewes were being put to the ram and at the dispersal sale in 1903 the top price for shearling ewes and six-tooths was paid by Sir Jeremiah Colman of **Gatton Park**, though many of the rams and ram lambs went to France.

Pagham Harbour blood was also to be found in Mr Edwin Ellis's famous **Summersbury** flock, founded in 1879, which won many successes at leading shows — including three champion prizes and the Prix d'Honneur for the best collection of sheep of any variety at the Paris International Show in 1889, and many prizes at American and Canadian shows as well. The Summersbury was dispersed in 1906, when King Edward VII paid some of the top prices for rams and six-tooth ewes in competition with the Duke of Devonshire.

The auction at Summersbury (which is by the North Downs at Shalford, near Guildford) was conducted by Messrs Stride & Son. Jeremiah Colman was in the chair: the flock had been replenished with some of Colman's best rams and ewes but it had originally been established on carefully selected ewes from Messrs Botting, with plenty of old Rigden blood from Hove, and in 1885 choice ewes and two famous rams (Merton and Ripon) had been acquired from Lord Walsingham's dispersal. Ellis's show successes were almost unrivalled in the history of the Southdown, or that of any other breed, and the sale catalogue, noting the flock's achievements, said:

> It may be asked, What is the reason or secret of this unparalleled and lasting success? Is the land at Summersbury specially rich or forcing for

Sheep? or is some special method of feeding employed? Neither is the case. The farm consists partly of the chalk downs, but mainly of thin, poor, elevated fields on the sand, and the Ewes have always to work hard for their living; a full head of Sheep being kept in proportion to the size of the Farm. There is no secret. The one and only reason is that the best Sheep of the breed were bought to start with, and the *best only* of their produce have been bred from ever since. Whenever a change of blood has been thought desirable, some of the best flocks have been drawn upon, and in one case a Ram was obtained from Mr Henry Webb at the price of 160 guineas.

As is well known, Mr Ellis has always taken as his model in breeding, the real true Southdown type — the short-legged, close-woolled Sheep, wide and deep and thick in carcase, whose hardy constitution enables it to thrive on the poorest pastures and which converts its food into the choicest Mutton and Wool the World produces.

By continuing year after year for more than a quarter of a Century to breed only from those animals which furnished the best example of the typical Southdown, the character and type has become fixed, and both Ewes and Rams may be relied upon to transmit to their descendants that superb quality and hardy constitution which they themselves have inherited, and which enables the Southdown to command the highest price and to secure the greatest profit of any breed of Sheep; whether they be kept on our Farms at Home, or on the limitless Prairies of our enterprising Colonial and Foreign Breeders.

This fine blast of the trumpet was followed by a detailed list of prizes won by the Summersbury, including at the Chicago World's Fair in 1893 — and the Southdowns proved to be of major interest at Chicago for many years. One of the prime Ellis rams, Summersbury Champion, had already been exported to Australia: the flock's blood was of international importance.

A few years later, in 1913, came the dispersal of the very famous **Babraham** flock by Mr C. R. W. Adeane. The flock had been established in 1885 and was of course closely associated with Jonas Webb and his descendants; his grandson, Fred Noel Webb, had managed the flock for many years. Its main blood was Buckland (Throckmorton), Goodwood, Gorringe and Streetly, and it won 282 prizes in the first 13 years of this century alone. Major buyers at the sale included Sir Jeremiah Colman and Mr John Langmead, and many sheep went to France, New Zealand and the United States.

The Langmead family are still well-known farmers and land owners along the south coast today. Their main Southdown flocks used to include the Flansham, the Wicks, the Selsey, the Bognor, the Ford, the Merston and the Preston Place. The **Preston Place**, founded in 1910 with selected ewes purchased from the estate of the late owner of Preston Place Farm (where the flock had been in existence for more than 70 years), was the flock of Walter J. Langmead who, with his brother John, was a major figure in the Southdown Sheep Society for many years. The foundation ewes in John Langmead's famous prize-winning **Ford** flock (which became the source of many exports) were purchased from several well-known West Sussex flocks between 1897 and 1901. John Langmead, who died in 1950, kept faith with the breed right through the dark war years. The flock passed to his nephew Walter (of Wicks, Yapton) who became a frequent winner of the Society's flock competitions and of many prizes at the annual Sussex County show. The flock was eventually sold, mainly to join B. D. Gough's **Barton** flock at Bury St Edmunds in Suffolk, but the young ewes were acquired by the Lady Jean Philipps to help form the **Parkgate** flock in Kent, and they were accompanied by shepherd Lewis Ward.

Walter's brother Leslie Langmead took over their father's sheep and ran the large **Merston** flock until he switched to the more commercial Dorset Downs; he frequently exported Southdowns to France before the Second World War. For many years the Merston shepherd was the invaluable Bob Mitchell, a man whose dedication was such that he would accept a Christmas lunch from the Langmeads' table but habitually ate it out in the fields with his sheep.

In Bedfordshire there was Lady Ludlow's notable **Luton Hoo** flock, established in 1897 and finally dispersed at the Southdown sale at Chichester in 1944. It was a major source of good rams, many being sold overseas to North America, Australia and New Zealand. Ewe lambs from the Luton Hoo, purchased in 1941, formed the foundation of the prize-winning **Berkhamsted**, which initially used Luton Hoo and Gaddesden rams. (The Halseys' **Gaddesden** was a well known post-war flock, and both Sir Walter Halsey and Captain Sir Thomas Halsey served as Presidents of the Society. The Gaddesden shepherd was Tom Fawkes). From 1949 the Berkhamsted, under the care of shepherd 'Nipper', used some famous Ford rams and the flock was further strengthened in 1954 by the purchase of the similarly bred **Hatch Gate**, winning most of the major show awards from 1947 until its dispersal in 1960 when the breeders Cooper, McDougall & Robert-

Pen of five shearling rams belonging to Lady Ludlow at the Chichester Show, 1937.
(*Sport and General*)

son Ltd sold their Home Farm at Little Gaddesden and ceased their farming activities altogether. In the meantime, however, they had exported Berkhamsted rams and ewes to New Zealand, Kenya, France, Ceylon and the Falkland Islands.

Another very famous flock was the **Eartham**, founded in 1852 by Mr George Oliver, transferred to Mr Bensted twenty years later and to Sir John Milbanke in 1900. The Eartham Farms, on poor hill land five miles north of Chichester, were taken over in 1905 by Mr John G. B. Stone, who also purchased the majority of the ewes and lambs, and three years later the flock and the estate were taken over by Sir William Bird, JP, who strengthened the flock with fresh female blood from well-known breeders of the time including Walter Langmead, H. Paynter, Alfred Heasman of Court Wick, Lord Northborne and others. Sir William also purchased expensive rams from the royal Sandringham flock, Sir Jeremiah Colman's Gatton Park, Lady Fitzgerald's Buckland, Lady Ludlow's Luton Hoo, Captain R. S. Hicks's Wilbraham

Mr Douglas McDougall and Mr Brian Gough at the 1962 Field Day, Moulton.
(*John Salter Photography*)

Temple, and from people like Walter and John Langmead, Edward Hobgen, C. R. W. Adeane at Babraham, the Duke of Devonshire and many more — the cream of the Southdowns of the period, in fact.

Because of the Eartham flock's environment, the aim was to breed a true hill type of ewe with a hardy constitution, good close fleece and 'well-turned leg of mutton', the sheep standing close to the ground and of an active nature, with the ability to be economical and rent-paying. It was a decidedly commercial flock, not pampered in any way, working hard for its living on the Downs by day and being folded on arable land at night. Although showing was somewhat restricted, the show yard was equally important and that was why blood was brought in from virtually every well-known Southdown flock of the first quarter of this century.

Sir William dispersed the flock in 1929. A quarter of a century later, in 1954, a new Eartham flock was started by Mr L. T. S. Hawkins, whose shepherd was Jimmy Cresswell (also with B.D. Gough's Barton flock) and whose manager was Sam Maxwell, a Scotsman born in East

The Eartham flock of Mr L. T. S. Hawkins: manager Sam Maxwell (*right*) with shepherd Horace 'Shep' Oliver and nine trophies. (*By kind permission, Mrs Vera Maxwell*)

Lothian who was originally a scientist with an agricultural degree and a lecturer in economics at Wye College, but who was also a thoroughly practical breeder of Ayrshire cows and a Southdown sheepman who knew the pedigree of every one of his best rams. He continued to give good advice to those who purchased the flock on its dispersal in 1976 — essentially J. & D. Humphrey, whose East Dean flock is described in the next section along with the flocks of other Eartham buyers such as Cyril Wise, J. & M. Craig, the Holdstocks, Miss Chandless, the Burdens and Mr P.A. Mummery. The Eartham sheep were quite large and robust, and there had already been some use of foreign rams in the flock before its dispersal. Maxwell died in 1981, when he was in his sixties, and the Society set up a prize fund in his memory. Not many members knew that he had also been captain of the English curling team, which trained on one of London's ice-rinks.

In 1953 Mr C. Goodger at last registered his longstanding flock at **Chidham**, near Chichester. The sheep were famous for the fineness

The Southdown Sheep

and tightness of their fleeces (a result of using Broadreed rams), their excellent conformation (from Langmead rams) and their great docility — a credit to 'Charlie' Goodger and his shepherd 'Tiny' Hubbard. That same year the Lady Jean Philipps established her **Parkgate** flock at Chelsfield in Kent, largely based on ewes from Chidham and also from the Grosvenor Hospital flock in Kent. Ford and Merston rams and the substantial number of ewes purchased from Walter Langmead helped to build up the flock and within ten years she was winning consistently at Findon, with the help of the Ford shepherd Francis Ward, a native of Hereford but who had worked with Southdowns for

Her Majesty the Queen admires Lady Jean Philipps's Southdown held by shepherd Lewis Ward at the Royal Show, Windsor, 1950. (*Coventry Standard*)

most of his life and who came to Parkgate in 1958. The flock went to Wales when Lady Philipps moved to Slebech Park, Haverfordwest, but has now been dispersed.

A recent dispersal was that of the **Upwaltham** of C. Chapman & Sons. Upwaltham Farm, which is near Petworth, is the highest farm in Sussex (up to 837 feet above sea level) and this important flock was established in 1927 when 200 sheep were taken over at valuation from Mr John Childs. Thirty draft replacement ewes were purchased in 1929 from Messrs Wyatt of Findon and fifty more from E. H. & H. H. Wadman of Sompting at Findon Fair in 1929 and 1930. A score of shearling ewes were bought at Chichester Show and Sale in 1931 from Mr Falkner of Dippenhall, Farnham, but thereafter all replacements were homebred. With the help of shepherd William Doughty (who had been at Dippenhall), the flock's show successes were many, including a first for wool at the Royal in 1955 and from the Masters of the Staple of England in 1959 and 1969. In 1957 the Chapmans bought the farm at Upwaltham and found themselves with 210 acres of woodland on the 1030-acre holding.

Greg Chapman, born in 1903 and still an annual visitor to Findon Fair, fondly remembers the Southdown as 'very beautiful sheep — there's nothing to touch them.' Although not originally a registered flock, it was always kept pure and he would cull his sheep quite drastically: many of the ewes proved not to have enough milk for rearing twins and any shearling ewe who could not make a reasonable job of her twins was not kept. About half the lambs were culled each year, with another 50% going in the following year, but he remembers with particular affection an old ewe who had eighteen lambs before succumbing to a bad prolapse. As a ten-year-old her mouth was still perfect and towards the end, when she was fifteen or sixteen years old, she could still chew mangolds with her back teeth as fast as they were sliced up for her.

The Upwaltham, which had some New Zealand Punchbowl blood, was finally dispersed at Findon Fair in 1973, when the Colmans started the Steepdown flock with Chapman stock. Another long established flock dispersed in recent years was the **Mundham**, near Chichester, which had been taken over by Mr R. S. Chitty from his father Arthur in 1951, when there were 165 ewes.

---— CHAPTER EIGHT ——

British Flocks Today

The oldest flocks still in existence are the Broadreed, the Ringmer, the Moulton, the Chailey and the Brynglas, all established for at least thirty years and all quite large. Other major flocks include the Camber Castle, Chetwynd, Cooden, Duncton, East Dean, Godshill, Oxney, Steepdown and Wootton. Flock size, of course, is not necessarily the most important criterion of influence, and smaller flocks such as the Fairlea in Scotland, the Greencross (with New Zealand blood), the Bemborough (selling especially to members of the Rare Breeds Survival Trust), the Ridings, the Bashurst, the Chilli and the Dingley, for example, are all worthy of note for one reason or another, including their influences on other flocks and their show successes. The most commercial among the newer group might be the East Dean and the Camber Castle: time will tell.

The **Broadreed** flock is now the oldest in the Southdown Flock Book and its story over the last few decades illustrates that of the breed as a whole. The present owner is Miss H. J. Paynter of Yielden, Bedford-shire, who is equally well known for her commercial herd of Dexter cattle. The flock was registered in 1898 by her grandfather, Henry Paynter, who came from Cornwall to Broadreed Farm in Sussex, near the Hampshire border, and purchased ewes from Mr J. W. Woods of Chilgrove and the Duke of Richmond at Goodwood. By the turn of the century the flock had built up to 400 ewes, including purchases from

Lord Northborne and Mr J. Tompkins, but during the late 1920s the number of ewes put to the ram was reduced to between 150 and 170 a year, though rams were being purchased from the top flocks of the day.

In 1933 the Broadreed flock was transferred to Henry's son, Harold B. Paynter, who moved from Sussex to north Bedfordshire at the beginning of the Second World War. Here the Ministry decreed that Southdowns were unsuitable for the region and refused to allow any rations for them so that the sheep had to survive on what could be found for them behind Paynter's new Suffolk flock. By a process of what was almost natural selection, therefore, the survivors formed the basis of a very hardy and thrifty flock and that strain remains much in evidence today. Indeed, it is essential that they are kept in on straw and water for six to eight weeks before tupping, in order to slim them down.

The Broadreed flock has always had an outstanding record for good wool and, as Ellman knew, good wool and good flesh go together. The lambs achieve top grades at slaughter and have retained the 'old-fashioned' Southdown shape. They are long in the body with a good spring of rib, all four legs set on square, the hind legs filled almost down to the hock with a tendency for double-muscling which is being encouraged by Miss Paynter, who took over the flock on her father's death in 1964. Great attention is being paid to shape; the head is small and neat while the ram's neck, as Miss Paynter puts it, is 'so short he can't turn and look at his rear end!' The wool is so tight that it is impossible to catch them by the fleece.

In the 1950s, as Miss Paynter remembers, all fleeces were individually graded and the Southdown's average wool density was a count of 62–63, second only to the Merino for fineness. With such wool quality, combined with small prime joints of lamb for the housewife and very low upkeep requirements for the farmer, the Broadreed flock looks to the future with considerable confidence.

The **Ringmer** flock at Gote Farm, not far from Lewes, was founded in 1921 by Captain John Christie of the Glyndebourne estate. By 1934 the Captain had become more interested in opera than in agriculture and he transferred the flock to his manager, John Craig, who was later awarded an OBE for services to agriculture. The flock was devastated by foot-and-mouth in 1937 but fortunately the Craigs were able to save sixty ewe lambs and the flock survived.

The original purchases were from Mr P. Martin, the Rt Hon. F. Huth Jackson, Messrs Edge & Gilmer, W. Brown, Percy Gorringe, C.

The Broadreed flock belonging to Mr H. B. Paynter of Knotting, Bedfordshire, 1953. (*Institute of Agricultural History and Museum of English Rural Life, University of Reading*)

Mr Frank Grantham, Chairman of the Society, with Mr Lewis Ward, shepherd to
Lady Jean Philipps, 1962 (*John Salter Photography*)

F. W. Sturgeon and J. C. Webber, and the flock's Woodhorn blood
traced back to the Luton Hoo. Today the female side is a closed flock
and the male breed lines used are Eartham, East Dean, Moulton,
Brynglas, Camber Castle and Steepdown. The Ringmer flock is still
substantial in numbers and is run on the South Downs and adjacent
land; breeding stock is sold at Findon and Ashford or privately, while
commercial stock goes to Lewes Market. There have been several

Ringmer firsts at Findon and successes, too, at the Royal. Frank Grantham's **Chailey** flock at Old Erringham Farm, Shoreham by Sea, was founded in 1954 with purchases of Ringmer stock from the Craigs, and also some sheep from Mr Percy Filkins.

John Craig died in 1980 and Mr D. J. Craig recalls his late father's methods for selecting breeding stock at a time when Kent farmers were beginning to complain about the growing numbers of barren ewes when Southdown rams were used. He and shepherd Jack Coleman (who was born on the farm) would draw out the largest lambs of either sex that met the Southdown criteria, and this method is still employed in the flock today. The Craigs have used French and New Zealand rams in order to get fresh bloodlines and size into their flock, with some success.

Like the Broadreed's, the Ringmer's story reflects some of the circumstances which have affected the breed, especially during and after the last war. The farm's downland is particularly steep and the family was unable to plough up the land during the war (it was anyway being used by the War Department) so that the flock was used instead to enrich the soil just below the Downs: it grazed short-term leys and the Downs in summer but was folded on thousand-headed kale in the winter and on any winter-proud wheat or barley (to help tillering). The leys were followed by winter wheat, and the kale by spring wheat or barley. However, with the advent of compound fertilisers and combined drills the need for the sheep grew less. The flock was reduced in numbers but retained to graze the Downs and put some heart into the thinner chalk fields by the use of long-term leys.

For many years John Craig and Percy Filkins were responsible for the preliminaries to the 'mock' judging of five ewes and five rams by Society members at the Field Days held on various breeders' farms all over Britain, instigated over thirty years ago. Mr Hugh T. Clark, owner of the Moulton flock, considers that these two men did the most to maintain the standard of the Southdown breed during the past forty years. Although neither of them did a great deal of showing or providing stud rams, they were always there to give advice and a guiding hand. Craig was a man of few words: as a judge, he did not need to say anything when he found a fault but simply looked up from under those heavy eyebrows which always reminded Clark of a Shorthorn cow — one up and the other down. If he did speak, his words counted. There can be few involved with the breed until recent

The Grand Flockmasters: Mr Percy Filkins and Mr John Craig, OBE, at the 1962 Field Day, Moulton. (*John Salter Photography*)

Mr Hugh T. Clark (Centenary President) with Mr Ken Ward and Mr Leslie Burt, at the 1962 Field Day, Moulton. (*John Salter Photography*)

times who have not benefited from the wisdom and guidance of Craig and Filkins, and Clark knows that even now, when he looks at a prospective stud ram or ewe, he thinks: 'Would John approve?'

Clark's **Moulton** flock, near Newmarket in Suffolk, was founded in 1950 when twenty shearling ewes were purchased from Captain R. H. Wagner and put to a Gawcombe ram. Forty ewes with lambs were purchased at the dispersal of the Sir R. Sothern Holland's flock from Westwell Manor at Burford in Oxfordshire. Today the Moulton is possibly the largest flock in Britain, with 120 ewes put to the ram in 1987. Clark is loyal to the traditional Southdown and has some of the best in the country. Recently he has started to increase the size of his sheep with carefully chosen East Dean blood but he is a most professional breeder and would never risk losing quality for the sake of quantity. His successes over the last forty years have been considerable and the Moulton has probably provided more foundation stock for new flocks than any other since the Second World War. Moulton sheep have been included in many important export consignments and they have been unequalled in the Flock Competition with eighteen wins in Class A and eleven Supreme Championships. At the Royal Show in recent years the flock has taken the Supreme Female award thirteen times, the Supreme Overall five times, the Miller Hallet Group five times and the Hazleton Cup on eleven occasions.

The **Brynglas** is one of the few Welsh flocks. Mr H. G. Hughes farms at Talgarreg, Llandyssul, in Dyfed and the flock was founded in 1958 with ewes purchased from Mr E. Low Beer. The sires used now are mainly of New Zealand origin (Tahrua and Greencross) or home-bred and East Dean rams, and the overall length within the flock is increasing.

The Isle of Wight is home to some good Southdown flocks, including one of the few really commercial ones in the country: the **Camber Castle** flock of David Randall at Ventnor, which was started in 1967 with Chidham ewes purchased from the estate of the late Charles Goodger. There are now about 100 ewes on 33 acres. The flock has done well in the show ring for several years and Randall firmly believes in the value of showing for the sake of promoting the breed as a whole. The main outlet is the sale of rams and ram lambs, especially as sires for ewe lambs. Randall points out that the Southdown cross is small enough at birth to be dropped easily and is much less hungry than, say, a Suffolk, so that the young mother is not required to give so much milk. This, combined with the lamb's quick maturity, makes less demand on the ewe lamb and gives her time to continue growing.

Camber Castle ram lambs are also in demand from mainland butchers. In 1989, for example, 120 pure Southdowns graded, all at 3L; indeed, a major supermarket chain admired the breed's fine bones and deep loin and expressed interest in large contracts for Southdown-sired crosses.

Also on the Isle of Wight is the **Godshill** flock, owned by Mr F. K. Mitchell and set up in 1975 with the purchase of the **Shalcombe** flock from Mr S. S. Ross, MP. Today the sires used include Camber Castle, Moulton and Ringmer.

Mr P. J. Ballard's **Cooden** flock at Little Common, Bexhill, was started in 1965 with 18 ewes purchased from Mr E. Latille-Campbell of St Leonard's Forest and a ram from Charles Goodger. The rams used since then include Ringmer, East Dean, Brynglas, Mundham and Barnhorn (the latter flock is owned by Mr J. H. Ballard) and the flock has had successes with its own rams at the South of England show. The **Steepdown**, another Sussex flock, was started in 1973 with the purchase of Upwaltham stock from Mr C. Chapman at the nearby Findon Fair. The flock's owner, Mrs Sheila Colman, has travelled widely and recently bought Southdowns in France: her comments on French and American Southdowns are reported in the section describing the breed overseas.

The **Fairlea**, at Collin by Dumfries, is one of the few Scottish flocks and is owned by Mr Cyril Wise. It was started in 1969 with Ashyardgate stock purchased from Mr J. Wyllie of Eaglesfield, Dumfriesshire, and the breed lines include Eartham, Brynglas, Ringmer and Ridings. Unfortunately there are no shows for Southdowns in Scotland but the flock has been successful at Findon and the rams have proved to be ideal sires on ewe lambs. The breed is very easy to manage and the lambs are hardy even on some of Scotland's higher farms. Mr Wise is breeding for length and good fleshing qualities so that the rams will produce crossbred lambs from commercial ewes without excessive fat cover. The Ringmer blood in the flock has ensured that the Fairlea sheep are indeed of excellent size.

The well-known Eartham sheep contributed to several other flocks, including the late Miss M. C. Chandless's **Sherington** at Selmeston, near Polegate, which was based on stock purchased from Hawkins in 1970. The **Stodmarsh** near Canterbury, recently dispersed, was based on Eartham ewes bought in 1974 and used East Dean and Brynglas sires. However, the major pool of Eartham blood today is in the **East Dean**: most of Hawkins's flock was purchased by Messrs J. & D. Humphrey at the dispersal in 1976 and the Eartham manager, Sam Maxwell, continued to advise the new owners, whose New House Farm was within a couple of miles of the flock's old home.

The sideboards at New House Farm are now laden with prizes, especially from Findon, Kent and Smithfield. The sheep are run on the Downs and the lowlands and are family-bred to provide high quality lamb with small-boned and well-fleshed carcases, and MLC recording figures are kept for this commercial flock. David Humphrey stresses the importance of recording in the interests of management and marketing and has proved that the Southdown can be a profitable and easily managed breed. The stocking rates are high and his lambing averages are 140–185% with very few lambing problems, even with the larger lambs now produced by the flock which average nearly 4 kg at birth, and some weigh more than 6 kg.

Taking Maxwell's advice, Humphrey sells more than half his output to Scotland. He shows regularly at various fatstock shows and is well aware of the importance of co-ordinated publicity for a breed which has so much to offer. He also appreciates the need to meet modern requirements for a bigger frame without losing the old Southdown qualities in the legs, wool, early maturity and general ease of management. Family butchers in particular like the lack of waste on a Southdown and Humphrey is achieving his aim of combining length with a good back end by introducing one or two new bloodlines. Performance is an important criterion in the East Dean flock and sales are now virtually throughout the country, including at Kelso in Scotland, in south Wales, and in Kent and Surrey as well as Sussex.

Mr P. A. Clementson's **Oxney** flock at Lydd, near Romney Marsh in Kent for most of its existence, is increasingly recognised for wool and carcase quality. It was started in 1976 with purchases from Mr J. Goodhew and Mr W. M. Chitty, and now Camber Castle and East Dean sires are used. In 1989 Clementson attended the World Wool and Sheep Congress in Tasmania and he beat every English Down breed there. He is an acknowledged expert on wool-growing in the eyes of the British Wool Marketing Board as well as within the Southdown world and is also recognised as an official judge of the breed.

Peter Clementson firmly supports the traditional 'English' type of

Southdown. Its conformation has won him many carcase competitions at Smithfield and various agricultural shows; its short, dense, fine wool enabled him to take the Kent Golden Fleece first prize for eight years as well as many other wool awards. He intends to introduce some Australian blood in the near future from lines which have retained the traditional 'back end' of the breed but are larger than the English type. In the meantime he has already proved that part-time sheep farmers can be as professional and successful as full-time commercial producers, which should greatly encourage the large number of smallholders who are now interested in Southdowns.

Among the part-timers is Mr D. C. Turner with his **Dingley** flock in Leicestershire. It is of recent origin, started in 1985 with Broadreed ewes purchased from Miss Paynter and a ram from Mr W. R. Garner. Breed lines include Godwick, Brant and Moulton and Mr Turner has demonstrated not only that small flocks can be successful (his show record is already excellent, especially at the East of England, the South of England, the RBST Show, the Derby County and the Royal) but also that very good Southdowns can be produced and promoted far from their native downland. He is also convinced that bloodlines already in Britain are more than adequate to produce excellent carcases which exactly match the current demand for small lambs of high conformation.

In contrast to Turner, Messrs P. A. and R. A. H. Whitcombe's **Greencross** flock relies on imported New Zealand stock originally purchased in 1979/80. The Greencross influence is spreading rapidly from its base at Churt in Surrey, largely by means of private sales. The breed lines include Gatton Park, Glen Isla, Tahrua and Glenrowan and the flock has won several first prizes in interbreed classes at local shows but cannot be shown at the Royal because of Maedi-visna accreditation. As a result of a visit to Australia early in 1990, there are plans to import semen from the flock of the Australian breeder Mr Geoff Baker (who purchased the bulk of the New Zealand Braemore flock belonging to Mr L. G. Mackay in 1980) as there seems to be considerable British interest in the longer, larger New Zealand type of Southdown.

The Whitcombes, already well-known breeders of pedigree Suffolks and Border Leicesters but not at that time involved with Southdowns, were asked to look at Southdowns on behalf of the Society on a visit to New Zealand in 1979 and were so impressed by their size, length and meatiness that, as well as selecting stock for the Society, they took the opportunity to buy a ram and four in-lamb ewes to start their own Southdown flock in Surrey. The flock is not lambed until the end of March and they achieve rates of nearly 200% lambs weaned to the number of ewes put to the ram. Shearing rams are sold for breeding and also for cross-breeding on commercial ewe hoggs. The New Zealand stock is producing the type of breeding ram the Whitcombes want, with good body length and also adequate leg length for tupping commercial ewes.

1980 also saw the establishment of the **Duncton** flock at the Northchapel farm of Mr D. G. Burden, based on draught Eartham ewes (in lamb to an Eartham ram) purchased from Mr F. H. Grantham and some shearling ewes from Mr W. M. Chitty's Mundham flock. A dozen draught ewes were purchased at Findon in 1983 from Mrs C. Hornung and Mrs H. L. Martin, including six Eartham-bred animals. At present the sires used include East Dean, Chailey and Ringmer rams and the Duncton now has more than seventy homebred ewes. The main outlet is prime lamb sold to Swift Meats of Petersfield in Hampshire and the number of lambs reared to weaning per ewes tupped is 1.83 (MLC figures). The flock's lambs achieve consistent wins at the Christmas carcase shows.

Mrs Sue Thomson's **Chetwynd** flock at Clayton, near Hassocks, was started in 1977 with stock from Mr C. G. King (Gunton and Parkgate) and W. M. Chitty (Mundham). From the original three sheep, the flock has increased to about sixty breeding animals and the breed lines include Parkgate, Burghley, Godshill and Moulton rams, with a recent preference for a Moulton ram kept as the most typical of the breed. This downland flock is bred for prolificacy and growth while maintaining the traditional Southdown conformation and looks, and any animal with hereditary faults is carefully culled. Ewes and ewe lambs are sold privately; entire ram lambs go to the local abattoir and all have graded, the meat being described as 'wonderful'. The ewes are all outwintered on the South Downs.

The **Ridings** flock at Herons Ghyll, to the north of Uckfield, was started in 1980 by Mr Paul Wakeham-Dawson, who was born and raised on the South Downs and was well acquainted with some of the old shepherds, especially Harry Coppard and Jack Coleman. After studying agriculture at Cirencester and Cambridge, he became an ADAS adviser in East Yorkshire (hence the flock prefix) and, after returning from a secondment to Kenya, he purchased some of the original type of larger Southdowns from the Craigs' Ringmer flock. He knew the shepherd of old and was aware that the type would have adequate milk to rear twins of good birthweight, in contrast to what he considered to be the dangerously small type with inadequate milk. His aim has been to maintain size (rather than increase it) by selection, using a line-breeding system with the help of Ringmer W10, son of the very prepotent Moulton ram H83.

Wakeham-Dawson's daughter Susan, now married to Mr Justin Harmer, became the fifth generation of shepherds in the family with her own **High Hurstwood** flock at Offham, near Lewes, using the Moulton ram D13, sired by a close Ringmer relation of H83. The principle outlet for both flocks is breeding stock sold at the RBST show and sale at Stoneleigh in September. Wakeham-Dawson sheep have been champions at the Royal Welsh and Surrey County, and reserve champions at the Royal and South of England, and there have been many other prizes too. The Ridings flock is in the High Weald, while the High Hurstwood is on the South Downs.

Paul Wakeham-Dawson wrote an article about the Southdown in *The Ark* (published monthly for its members by the Rare Breeds Survival Trust) which has been of great value in compiling the breed's history and continuing development for this Centenary book.

CHAPTER NINE

Shepherds

The shepherd is half the flock. You can buy any sheep you like but you can't buy a shepherd. [Leslie Langmead, 1990]

The traditional folding of sheep on the downs and arable lands of the east and south of England maintained the fertility of thin chalky and sandy soils, relieved western and northern hill farms of sheep-wintering, and virtually created that unique character, the downland shepherd.

For several centuries sheep were essential to the downland farms and their shepherds were men of great skill, knowledge and self-sufficiency, accustomed to keeping their own company and relying on their personal judgement. Local farmers were wisely content to leave sheep management to the shepherds but, gradually, another agricultural revolution stole up on them and there are very, very few genuine downland shepherds today, either active or retired. They have quietly faded away, disenchanted by the new type of farmer they used to call the 'sheerman' (shireman) or 'furriner' — farm owners who were not Sussex people but had moved in from other counties, who did not appreciate the shepherd's downsmanship and were more concerned with lamb prices than husbandry. In former days, shepherds had been consulted and were expected to say what they needed for their sheep but later they were instead ordered, told what to do and how, and expected to get the flock into condition on whatever the boss would spare them. Worse, whereas formerly the sheep were of a locally suitable breed, later *any* sheep was expected to thrive and make a profit anywhere, the new farmers failing to appreciate that breeds have been created specifically to meet local needs and conditions.

In 1929 the *West Sussex Gazette* published a letter from James Ford, 'Ex-Supt., W. S. C.', of Easebourne, near Midhurst, who had been associated with shepherds many years earlier. His recollections went right back to the time of the West Sussex Agricultural Society, founded in 1835, which held its annual event at Goodwood. An important part of the event was the awarding of prizes to shepherds and during the 1860s Ford recalled men like Henry Denyer, shepherd to the Duke of Richmond 'and a valued servant', and William Denyer who was shepherd to Mr J. Attwick Pinnex of West Dean. He explained: 'The shepherd was not the smock frock rustic imagined by the "towny", but was invariably an intelligent, thrifty and useful man.' His own father, shepherd for 30 years for Mr William Turner, Hipkin, Colesworth Farm, West Dean, was awarded several prizes at Goodwood, including £4 for rearing the greatest number of lambs in one year from a flock of 300 ewes, and another for 'having, previous to his marriage, made a provision for his future maintenance in life' by saving £30. (Ellman would have approved!) He bought himself a new watch for four guineas and a grandfather clock for five guineas from Mr Joseph Wilson of East Street in Chichester.

James Ford took a prize himself in 1862, 'and went home with a gold coin in my pocket and a laurel twig, handed by the Chairman to each prizewinner on taking his prize.' He also mentioned George Barber of Chilgrove, who worked for Squire Woods and was paid 12 shillings a week at most but managed to save £15, a watch worth £4 and furniture worth £6.

The principal event at the annual meeting, however, was the sheep-shearing competition held under the cedar trees in the Park. Each man had to shear six full-grown, heavily fleeced Southdown sheep. Later, the dinner and prize-giving were held in the Tennis Court, Water-beach, and a band would precede the entry of the Duke of Richmond, the Bishop of Chichester, Lord March, Lord Lennox and about three hundred others. Many years before, it was recorded, His Grace (who took the chair at the dinner) travelled from London after an all-night sitting in the House of Lords; he left the room at 7 o'clock and the chair was taken by Captain Pilkington, and 'the company maintained the conviviality and harmony until a late hour'.

By 1937, the *West Sussex Gazette* was already lamenting that the old type of Sussex shepherd was fast dying out. 'Before long,' it declared, 'his ways and habits will have become legendary to a new generation.' An effort was therefore made to collect and preserve at Worthing Museum the 'gear' which the old Sussex shepherds had used. They included a fine dark grey linen smock made by a Falmer woman before the turn of the century, in perfect condition and a good example of 'the needlecraft which at one time was the pride of every Sussex village woman's heart'. There was an old home-made stool, something like a wooden shooting-stick, made and used for twenty years by shepherd G. Newell of the Devil's Dyke. There was a pair of Findon shepherd Tom Rushbridge's 'false-tongues', which were detachable leather tongues worn over the front of his boots to protect them from the dew and damp herbage. Shepherd John Norris of Coate Farm, Durrington, had contributed his formidable home-made cudgel, very necessary in the days when rough characters were frequently encountered on isolated parts of the Downs. Shepherd Michael Blann of Patching, who had died three years earlier at the age of 90, was remembered by his beautiful horn lantern and other implements included a shepherd's umbrella more than four feet in diameter when open, a Pyecombe marking iron, trailing-irons from Sompting, wooden and iron shackles, a home-made wooden thatching needle and a Goring dirt-knocker which was used to remove caked mud from ewes' fleeces.

Shepherds were often craftsmen of some versatility. The writer and artist Phoebe Somers, describing several shepherds in the county magazine *Sussex Life* in 1986, tells of Charles Wadey of Ebernoe whose skills included thatching, rush-cutting, lawn laying, woodland work, faggot bundling, fencing, the making of ash bends for barrels and clog-soles from alder and osier. The clogs, with leather straps and toecaps, were sold for a shilling and a penny.

Phoebe Somers talked to many shepherds, and drew their portraits. She described Jack Beecher of Aldingbourne, who claimed that there was no healthier smell than that of his sheep in their pens on a frosty morning and who used traditional ways of counting his flock with old Gaelic words. Cyril Matcham of Poling told her about his own 'dirt knocker': he simply crushed clumps of dried mud on the fleece between two pieces of wood before the sheep was pushed into the wash. The sheepwash at Wepham sounds quite adventurous: it was fed from the Arun, a strongly tidal river which raised the level of the dip (known as The Splash) twice a day. Two men would be suspended in barrels (anchored to posts) in midstream, rising and falling with the tide as they controlled the sheep swimming past them, grabbing them to rub the wool by hand and then dunking them under the water.

One of the earliest 'characters' on record was John Dudeney, born at Plumpton Cottage in 1782 and from a long line of shepherds. His story is told by Esther Meynell in her book about Sussex published in the late 1940s. Dudeney was, literally, a 'perusing man', a term once used of Sussex shepherds to suggest that they slowly and carefully thought over the things they knew. But John Dudeney was a voracious reader, buying his books with his savings from his wages of £6 a year while at

Sheep-washing in the river Arun at Burpham, West Sussex. The washer stood in a barrel to keep dry but, even so, it was a cold, wet job and many washers suffered from rheumatism as a result. (*West Sussex County Library Service*)

Kingston, near Lewes, where he became under-shepherd to a flock of 1400 sheep when he was seventeen years old. He would take his books with him on the Downs and dig a hole in the turf for them and his slate and pencil, covering this portable study with a large stone. He studied French, geography, mathematics and astronomy but on Sundays he read only the Bible and even taught himself Hebrew so that he could read it in its original language. In 1804 his love of books overwhelmed his love of sheep and he went to Lewes to join Baxter, the printers of the *Library of Agricultural and Horticultural Knowledge* and the *Memoirs of Ellman*. Later he became a teacher and was still teaching a few weeks before he died in 1852 at the age of seventy.

Another famous nineteenth-century character was Stephen Blackmore, who is described in some detail in Arthur Beckett's *The Spirit of the Downs*, published in 1909. Blackmore, shepherd at East Dean, presented the Sussex Archaeological Society's museum with a collection of some 700 Neolithic flint implements — celts, hammer-stones, scrapers, flakes and chisels — which he had gathered on the Downs around East Dean.

A great favourite among camera-happy tourists between the wars was old George Chant of Angmering, shepherd for several decades on Mr Oscar Pyle's Southdown Farm and born at Up Marden, near Harting. With his cheerful face and shaggy beard, he was indeed photogenic and was the subject of many of George Garland's photographs in the 1930s. The Garland collection is now at the West Sussex Records Office in Chichester and is a marvellous record of shepherding techniques and characters of the period.

While there were still good shepherds of the old kind out on the South Downs, their company, memories and advice were sought and recorded by Barclay Wills. Wills was a compassionate and careful observer, writer, photographer and artist who bequeathed a rich treasury of downland atmosphere, wildlife and practical details. Some of Wills's work was collected by his biographer, Shaun Payne, and published recently in a delightful book, *The Downland Shepherds*, edited with the help of Richard Pailthorpe of the Weald and Downland Open Air Museum and enhanced with paintings by Gordon Beningfield, the well-known countryside artist and admirer of Southdown sheep. The book also contains evocative period photographs by George Garland.

Born in Islington in 1877, the Cockney lad christened Harry Barclay Wills was a passionate lover of the countryside and professionally published his wildlife illustrations when he was in his early twenties, gleaning material from the heaths and small wildernesses of north London and later from the New Forest and other parts of Hampshire. As a young man he soon discovered the South Downs and in the 1920s he moved from London to Brighton so that he could ramble widely over the downs, always alert for the sound of sheep bells, which drew him like a will o' the wisp.

He wrote about his long conversations with a generation of shepherds born in the 1850s and 1860s, some of them almost old enough for their lives to overlap with those of Coke of Norfolk and Webb of Babraham, if not Ellman of Glynde himself. Most of them were born in Sussex and remained in the county all their lives, some on the same stretch of downland for decades.

There was Nelson Coppard, born at Poynings in 1863, whose father had been a shepherd before him on Dyke Hill for nearly twenty years. Like many a shepherd, Nelson moved around locally: he started as a shepherd boy at Horton, near Beeding, then became a teg boy at Patcham, an under-shepherd at Seddlescombe and later a shepherd at Truleigh, Iford, America (between Newhaven and Firle), Balmer (near Falmer), Mary Farm at Falmer and Pangdean Farm by Clayton Mills near Pyecombe, a village famous for the shepherd's hooks or crooks made at Berry's forge by the church. (Phoebe Somers met the Pyecombe crook-maker Charles Mitchell when he was ninety: she describes him as 'like a very lively gnome, full of fun' and tells a nice little story to illustrate his sense of humour.)

There were several Coppard shepherds, including Frederick and his son Harry Charles, the latter born in 1887 at Patcham and later known as Henry, who was one of the last of the downland shepherds and became a popular subject for photographers after the Second World War, when he worked at Water Hall Farm and Court Farm. When he died in 1963 he was given a long obituary in *The Times*.

Mary Farm at Falmer had also employed Tom Rusbridge, who lived at Nepcote (home of Findon Fair) when Wills met him in the 1920s. He was born at West Firle in 1856 and began working when he was seven years old, first at Bosham then at Wick Farm in Ditchling, Hill Barn Farm at Southwick, and finally at Findon Park. He was a singer and musician and he taught his daughter, Grace, to play the melodian.

Shepherding and music go well together. There was the singing flautist Michael Blann of Patching, born at Beeding in 1843, who also

Shepherd Nelson Coppard.
(*Barclay Wills*)

Shepherd Michael Blann.
(*West Sussex County Library Service*)

Shepherd Tom Rusbridge.
(*Barclay Wills*)

Shepherd George Humphrey.
(*Barclay Wills*)

played a tin whistle and jew's harp and who died at the age of ninety, having been a shepherd since he was nine years old. George Humphrey of Sompting (born in 1864 at Canada, near West Dean, West Sussex) was the grandson of the Duke of Richmond's shepherd at Boxgrove; Charles Trigwell of Shoreham, born in 1851 at Hove, was famous for his smile, while Charles 'Darkie' Funnell of Wilmington wore gold earrings that added an exotic touch to his picturesque white hair and dark, gipsy-like face. Frank Upton had been shepherd at Brown's Farm at West Blatchington for fifty years when Wills knew him and it seems that farmer John Brown, who also farmed at Patcham, Standean, Ditchling and Rottingdean, had 5000 breeding ewes in all at the time. John Brown was one of three farming Browns (the others were at Lewes and Friston Place) named by shepherd William Duly of East Dean, who was born at Alciston in 1858 and who also mentioned other old farmers like Hart of Beddingham, Saxby of West Firle and Madgwick of Alciston. George Bailey of Beeding Court Farm at Steyning was unusual in that he was born in Wiltshire in 1856 but he came to Sussex when he was only three years old and remained at Beeding Court for forty-six years.

Although Henry Coppard is perhaps famous as one of the last downland shepherds, it was only in July 1989 that old 'Shep' Oliver died. He was a well-known and well-loved Sussex character who had, as it happened, been interviewed the previous autumn at Findon Fair (an event he never missed in seventy-five years) for BBC Television in a programme which was broadcast on the night he died. He was born at West Marden in 1902 and christened Horace Percy Oliver, one of the thirteen children of shepherd James Oliver, who was himself the son and grandson of shepherds. Horace began working with sheep when he was twelve, in partnership with his father at Peppering Farm, above Amberley, and they worked together for more than thirty years. Later he joined his sister Ethel in charge of 500 Clun Forest ewes at Court Hill Farm, Slindon, but after ten years they both went to look after the famous Eartham flock of Southdowns and moved with the flock to New House Farm, East Dean, when the sheep were bought by Mr David Humphrey in 1976. 'Shep' finally retired in 1988 but in the meantime 'his' sheep won major prizes all over the country and he had also become known to a less professional public by giving regular hand-shearing demonstrations at the Weald and Downland Open Air Museum at Singleton.

His brother Frank Oliver, of Houghton, used his great-grandfather's old crook for sixty years on the Downs and he told Phoebe Somers of an anxious moment for him at Findon Fair. He had prepared his sheep beautifully the day before and they were all spotlessly groomed when he penned them for the night beneath some trees. At dawn, when he came to start their drive to Findon, he found that the sheeps' fluffy white backs were splattered with blue: they had unwittingly spent the night right under a large starling roost. Yet the flock still managed to take first prize.

There were many other 'characters' on the Downs. Some have been interviewed by Shaun Payne and Richard Pailthorpe; others have been recorded in writing and in portraits by Phoebe Somers and others, and some have been recorded on tapes kept in county archives. East Anglian shepherds also played their part in the story of the Southdown sheep, of course, though today there are so few flocks in a region that once boasted such famous Southdown breeders as Coke of Holkham and the Webbs of Babraham.

Hugh Clark of Newmarket recalls many Southdown shepherds since the war, all of them masters of their craft in the day-to-day care of their flocks and in the preparation of sheep for shows and sales. Most of the men had come up the hard way, starting as an under-shepherd or teg boy for many years before taking on the post of head shepherd, and many came from a long line of shepherds, including Ted Duly, one of Clark's shepherds: Duly's family of five brothers, all of them Southdown shepherds, traced back to a Duly with John Ellman's flock. Sidney Bone, another Moulton shepherd, had been with the Hazleton (owned by Wing Commander R. Grant Ferris, now Lord Harvington) along with Bill Adlem, who was also shepherd to the Bloxworth (Roland Harris). Men such as Jack Colman (Ringmer), Jimmy Cresswell (Eartham), Tom Fawkes (Gaddesden), 'Tiny' Hubbard (Chidham), Bob Mitchell (Merston) and Lewis Ward (Ford and Parkgate) have already been mentioned. Others of the period 1945 to 1970 included Jack Cole, who was shepherd to the Westwell (Westwell Estates) and Harold B. Paynter's Broadreed, Harry Fawkes of the Wrotham flock (The Lady Elizabeth Byng), Bob Savage of the Blackheath (Major Vernon Wentworth), Philip Wadsman of the Gawcombe (Captain Wagner) and the Lackford (D.W.P. Gough), and Reg Munford of the Barton (B.D. Gough) and the Abbotsleigh (Roger Hales), a flock also once shepherded by Moulton's Ted Duly

Mr Ted Duly, last of a long line of Southdown shepherds to the Clark family, 1959.
(*Mary Clark*)

who must surely have been related to the nineteenth-century William Duly of East Dean, known to Barclay Wills.

In Sussex today, the old ways are given a setting at the Weald and Downland Open Air Museum at Singleton, where the sound of sheep bells can still be heard from a small Southdown flock. Visitors can see a restored shepherd's hut and shepherd's room, in addition to the many rescued historic buildings from South East England reconstructed at the museum. The sheep graze in fields enclosed by pleached fences and they lamb in traditional yards protected by thatched hurdles and wattles, just as the old shepherds would remember.

CHAPTER TEN

Managing a Southdown Flock

Any breed, however good, can only give of its best with appropriate management, which involves sound basic husbandry, a thorough appreciation of the breed's particular qualities and needs, and an understanding of market requirements. Too many people dismiss a breed for the wrong reasons; too often the fault lies more with a lack of stockmanship or marketing techniques than a failing in the breed. No breed is perfect, of course, and the art is to exploit its good qualities while minimising the effects of any drawbacks.

In the case of the Southdown, for example, too many people say (without thinking) that it is too small, that the lambs are difficult to sell or grade, or that they become too fat, forgetting that any animal gets too fat if it is wrongly managed, whatever its breeding, and forgetting to balance the positive virtues of the Southdown's compact conformation.

The following sections are designed above all to give guidance to those who are new to Southdowns, particularly the increasing number of part-time farmers, though it could be that full-time commercial flockmasters will also glean useful information from the management tips suggested here by some well-known members of the Southdown Sheep Society.

Before considering current and future management techniques, there is still something to be learned from the flockmasters of the past, especially outstanding breeders and stockmen such as Ellman who knew their livestock very well indeed. First, then, here are some hints from the past.

ELLMAN'S TOUCH

Writing after his retirement from active farming, and not long before he died in 1832, John Ellman contributed a comprehensive article on the breeding, rearing and general management of sheep in general, and the Southdown in particular, in Baxter's *Library of Agricultural and Horticultural Knowledge*.

Before entering into details of the general management of his Southdowns, he first described and assessed fifteen breeds and then considered the basic look and feel of the best type of sheep, whatever its breed. The major points, to his excellent stockman's eye, were as follows — and it should be borne in mind that the term 'fatten' means 'finish' rather than adding layers of fat!

Qualities constituting a disposition to feed

1. THE SHEEP MUST BE WELL BRED, i.e. THE OFFSPRING OF PARENTS POSSESSED OF GOOD QUALITIES. I would rather breed from an indifferent ewe and ram, that I knew to be well bred, than from a ewe or ram possessing a good external shape derived from an indifferent stock, where little or no attention had been paid to the breeding.

2. THE SHAPE OR SKELETON MUST NOT BE TOO LARGE FOR THE KEEP, nor should the size of the bone be large and coarse. This is a consideration of great importance, nor would I recommend the other extreme, as was the practice with the breeders of the new Leicester sheep, particularly the late Mr Bakewell: although Nature should be assisted, yet, in counteracting her laws, an injury is generally sustained. The new Leicester sheep were bred in my time so small in the bone, and consequently became so delicate in constitution, that many ewes could not rear their own lambs: here was an instance where fineness of bone was an injury. The other extreme is equally inimical: a requisite proportion of bone is necessary to render the sheep sufficiently hardy to bear both changes of season and keep, it being totally impossible for any breeder at all times and seasons to give his sheep an equal quantity of feed throughout the year. The alternations of heat and cold cannot be

avoided; consequently, breeders must see the necessity of breeding sheep sufficiently hardy to withstand these casualties.

3. THE PROPER PROPORTIONS OF PARTS, OR THE MAKE OF THE SHEEP, INDICATES A GOOD DISPOSITION. A well-proportioned animal is the best criterion of a good constitution and aptitude to fatten; in proof of which the Spanish sheep, which, when compared with any of the improved English breeds, are very ill-shaped, and handle hard under the skin, are very deficient in fattening qualities, so much so that but very few graziers have been enabled to make them fat.

4. SHEEP HANDLING SOFT AND MELLOW IN THE FLESH, IS A GOOD CRITERION OF A GOOD DISPOSITION TO FEED. This is too much neglected both in sheep and cattle; those of the best disposition to feed handle soft and mellow under the skin, which should not be thick or very thin; a thin skin indicates delicacy.

5. THE COUNTENANCE OF SHEEP IS AN INDICATION OF A GOOD OR BAD DISPOSITION, QUIETUDE HAVING MUCH TO DO WITH THE FATTENING QUALITIES. Sheep with large heads are seldom found to fatten very well; they may be hardy, and bear the changes of the seasons and keep without wasting much in flesh, but they have not much propensity to fatten when turned into good keep. I have found by experience that delicate animals generally fatten quicker when on good keep, and are the soonest reduced by bad keeping. This induces me to think that both extremes are bad, and that it is highly necessary that sheep should have a good constitution, as well as a disposition to feed. A well-formed animal is a criterion of both. It is also necessary to adapt the constitution somewhat to the soil and climate, as it would be folly to breed sheep too delicate and incapable of bearing the cold, when intended to stock the South Downs and other exposed, bleak situations, where the pasture is so short that the sheep must work all day to satisfy themselves with food; and on the other hand it would be equally absurd to give the same constitution to sheep intended for the richest pastures (there to fatten at an early period) where they would fill themselves in half an hour, and then lie down to rest. These cannot be bred too delicate or kept with too much quietude.

Ellman then considered in depth the best skeletal shape and the reasons for his choice. For example:

HEAD. The smallness of a sheep's head is an indication of its being well-bred ... Sheep with large heads generally experience great difficulty in lambing, and always indicate a want of aptitude to feed. The size also indicates a coarseness of bone and skin ... I can see no merit in a very prominent eye; I rather admire a tolerably full bright-looking eye, but the eye-cup, or bone, should not project [Ellman considered it led to losses at lambing time] ... Sheep should be well covered with wool on the forehead and especially between the ears, as it is a great protection against the fly.

NECK. The neck should be neither too long nor too short, but thin next to the head and tapering towards the shoulders, where it should be broad and straight on the top, and not what is generally called ewe-necked ... A long thin neck ... denotes delicacy.

THE BREAST. The breast should be wide and deep, projecting forward before the fore-legs. This is considered an essential point with graziers, as the breast gives the sheep a greater degree of weight, and also indicates a good constitution and disposition to feed ...

BACK AND LOINS. The chine should be low and straight from the shoulders to the setting on of the tail. The ribs should project horizontally from the chine, in which case the animal will lay its meat on the prime parts. The loin should be broad and flat. The sides high and parallel, as wide at the fore-end as at the hind, enabling the first rib to spring out well, which rib should project rather more than the others. The rump should be long and broad, the tail set on high and nearly on a level with the chine. The hips should be wide, the space between the first rib and hip-bone should be as narrow as possible, thus preventing the dropping of the belly. The ribs should be circular like a barrel.

LEGS. The legs should be neither very long nor very short; the hind leg ought to be full in the inside, at the point called the twist, the hock or hough turning rather out .... The fore-legs should be straight from the breast to the foot, and not what is termed knock-kneed.

WOOL. It is the opinion of many, that sheep which produce fine wool are finer and better in the meat than those of coarse fleeces, and this I think is borne out by the fact of fine-woolled sheep selling at better prices per pound in the market, on account of their mutton giving greater satisfaction to the consumers.

Next, Ellman turned his attention to general management, including selective breeding, then management of the ewe in pregnancy and during and after lambing. Here is a condensed version of his recom-

mendations, and, again, there are points both practical and philosoph-
ical which remain relevant today:

1. COUPLING THE MALE AND FEMALE. Previous to the coupling
of the sheep, the master should examine, in the minutest manner, both
male and female, but more particularly the male ... Upon examination,
he will no doubt find some great defect in the ewes in some particular
part, which should be remedied by putting a ram with them that is well
formed in those parts wherein the ewes are defective; but in doing this,
the greatest care must be taken lest a greater defect be introduced in
some other part, from a want of attention to the general formation of the
ram. I have frequently known, that whilst the breeder has been
attempting to eradicate one defect, a greater has been introduced ... but
should the breeder not have in his possession a ram suited for his
purpose, it would be advisable to hire one of another breeder who has
developed greater attention to the subject. By this practice, a number of
good ram lambs may be produced, and the best should be selected to
match with the best ewes, which, if used for two or three seasons, a great
improvement in the stock will be manifested.

There is one remark, however, I would offer to all breeders; — 'be not
too partial to your own sheep', as it has operated much in preventing
many from making improvements in their flocks.

It is too frequently the practice with shepherds, to save the rams from
ewes which are the best nurses, regardless of their shape or constitution.
This should not be done by shepherds; the master should superintend it
himself, as it is of the greatest importance.

In no case should ewes be used for breeding that possess any
hereditary disease, ... the defects will increase in the progeny.

I have generally observed, that sheep struck with fly one year, are
invariably so the next, and will continue so for succeeding years; they
should therefore be withdrawn from the flock ...

2. THE GENERAL MANAGEMENT TILL LAMBING. The rams in
Sussex are put with the ewes during the last fortnight in October, or the
first week in November; they are generally suffered to run with the ewes
for about five weeks ...

3. KEEP AND TREATMENT OF THE EWES, A SHORT TIME
BEFORE, AT, AND AFTER LAMBING. If it is wished that the ewes
should produce twins, they should be kept better than usual, before and
at the time the ram accompanies them; but if the land is not such as to
enable the breeder to keep the ewes that produce twins better than the
general flock while they suckle, it is not desirable to attempt to have

twins by that means. Another mode may however be adopted, that is, by saving twin ram lambs; experience has satisfied me that a ram which may be a twin, would get double the number of twin lambs than other rams. Twin-getting is hereditary in the rams.

Care should be taken that the ewes are not supplied too plentifully with keep for three or four weeks previous to their lambing, as, if they are in a too thriving state at the time of lambing, their blood becomes inflamed, and gangrene frequently follows in a few days after parturition. The shepherds generally fall into a mistake by supposing that if the ewes are not kept rather better a short time before lambing, they will not have so much milk for their young. In five or six days after lambing, however, it will be necessary to keep them somewhat better.

The most important job for the breeder — and the most remunerative for those with skill and judgement — was deemed by Ellman to be the sorting of his sheep, which he insisted should be undertaken by the master rather than the shepherd because the latter had a partiality to their flock and 'their ideas of perfection seldom extend beyond their own flock, and hence the principal cause why improvements in the South-down sheep have not been more progressive'. Ellman suggested that 80 to 100 ewes should be allotted to each ram (forty only for lamb rams), each lot of ewes being marked with pitch to differentiate them once the flock was reunited, and the lambs should likewise be marked with tiver soon after they were dropped so that, at the time of cutting, they could be ear-marked after their sires. In the following year the young ewes could be separated according to their ear-marks before being penned with the rams according to what breeders called 'get', so that the master could ascertain the respective merits of the rams. Wether lambs were sold in the autumn at about six months old.

This section was followed by attention to methods of raising and feeding artificial food for sheep and lambs on a downland farm: in early spring, after lambing, rye (sown in September on a clean fallow) would be fit for feeding ewes in April but should not be fed for many days together in case it caused scouring. The rye should last until the latter end of May before running to seed, when it could be ploughed for turnips or rape. Swede turnips should be sown in May, or mid-June at the latest. Ryegrass, 'the soundest food we can give', followed the feeding of rye and would take a downland flock through to the end of June, when winter tares would be ready to feed off (sown from the beginning of October to the beginning of the following May), and next came clover or 'rape' (the latter called cole in some counties, and nothing to do with the oil-seed rape seen today). Tares, clover and rape were usually sown preparatory to wheat.

On the South Downs, turnips were sown in abundance so that there was not only winter keep for sheep but also yard food for working oxen and youngstock. Swede turnips lasted until lambing but were not recommended after lambing as the lambs did not do well when ewes were on swedes.

Ellman makes the point that, to prevent the 'many disorders which afflict sheep', it was necessary to keep them in 'an equal state of flesh throughout the year, and not as is the practice of some flock-masters, who at one season make their sheep half fat, and at another time half starve them'. He therefore stressed the importance of always raising a sufficiency of keep for the flock throughout the year, a matter in which the Downs farmer had the advantage. On some farms sheep could be kept on the Downs for the greater part of the year and required but little artificial food.

Ellman devoted a major section to wool:

> As wool is an essential article with those farmers who keep large flocks of sheep, I would recommend them not to confine themselves to the growth of fine wool only, but to pay attention as well to the weight of the fleece, as this is now become the primary object with the purchaser. It is therefore desirable that both weight and fineness of pile should be combined ... : although I do not mean to say that South-down sheep will produce long-combing wool like those in Romney-marsh or Lincolnshire, as the pasture on the South-downs precludes the possibility of such a result; but if the Romney-marsh sheep were to be fed exclusively on the Downs, a decrease in the length of pile must necessarily be the consequence. That the production of the wool is modified by the nature of the keep cannot be doubted; for when South-down sheep are taken from the Downs, and put on rich pastures, their wool becomes much longer and heavier.
>
> The method to improve the length and fineness of the wool is ... to weigh the fleeces of the rams, and use those rams only which grow the heaviest wool, if fine, attention being paid at the same time to the shape and constitution of the rams ... How few breeders are there who pay sufficient attention to the frame of a sheep! — one looks at the head and colour of its face, another observes the neck, and the attentions of most are directed to one particular point: and should it please their fancy, they conclude the sheep to be good, while in other parts it may be

particularly defective. It is thought by most breeders, that sheep of the same breed, possessing the finest wool, fatten the quickest. I have stated before, that it is essential for sheep to be covered with wool about the head and particularly between the ears, as a protection against the fly, which otherwise much annoys them; in addition to which, I like to see a tuft of wool on the forehead, also the belly should be well covered beneath, down to the hock and knee, and I have no objection to see a little on their legs, between the knee and the foot. When they are bare of wool under the belly, it causes a great diminution in the weight of the fleece.

MANAGEMENT BETWEEN THE WARS

The first edition of *The Southdown Sheep*, published by the Society in 1922, printed in Chichester and edited by the well-respected journalist E. Walford Lloyd (who was the breed's official publicity officer), gave detailed advice on the management of a Southdown flock in different situations — on a South Downs hillfarm, on a low-lying arable farm on heavy land, and on the lighter soils of the eastern counties.

On the poor, thin, calcareous soils of the chalk hills, the ewes ran on the Downs by day, 'cropping the close, thyme-scented herbage — which diet is said . . . to be the cause of the delicate flavour possessed by Southdown mutton.' At night, in September, the downland ewes were folded on mustard or old clover leys but would be flushed for the tup (to promote twinning rates) by nightly folding on cabbage, rape or early turnips in the last two weeks of September, the diet being supplemented with half a pint of crushed peas or oats.

Ram-breeding flocks were managed for early lambs, as it was considered that the earliest a ram lamb was born, the better a sheep he would become, and the rams would join the ewes during the second week of September. In other flocks, however, red-raddled rams were turned in with the ewes on 1 October at a rate of one ram to every fifty ewes. The red-ochre raddle was changed to blue at the end of the month.

During October and November the folding pattern continued as before except that stubbles were substituted when the leys were ploughed for wheat. By the end of November the rams had been separated from the flock and the ewes were being folded on the remains of mangold foliage after the roots had been lifted for the clamp. If the weather turned very wet or cold towards the end of the month, the ewes would be given cribs of hay (four trusses for every hundred ewes) or, in really bad hay years, a mixture of oat straw and pea haulms.

The ewes continued to run on the Downs by day until the end of January, being folded on the arable land at night (rape, then old turnips by the New Year) but by the end of January they were kept close to home, only grazing the Downs nearest the fold, and by mid-February they were kept entirely in the fold while the shepherd built the lambing-yard. The yard was protected from north and north-east winds by a couple of long, low thrashed-out oat ricks, against which thatched hurdles were arranged in a square, two hurdles high, secured to a framework of stout ash uprights and lashed crosspoles which supported a roof of more thatched hurdles. Within this snug yard,

Traditional Southdown lambing fold in the 1930s, near Storrington, West Sussex.
(*George Garland Collection, West Sussex County Record Office*)

short-stay ewe coops were built, one hurdle deep by half a hurdle wide for each ewe and her lamb, and were well littered with straw.

On the other side of the rick wall a second yard was built to accommodate the animals when the lambs were a few days old, with a separate yard for ewes with twins. Close by would be the shepherd's mobile house, fully equipped for lambing, with a galvanised bin well stocked with cake and plenty of sweet hay protected from the weather by thatched hurdles and a tarpaulin. (The flocks offered an important outlet for those who worked the local hazel and chestnut coppices, producing all manner of wattles and sheep hurdles, a trade which is now slowly being revived after some very lean years.)

As lambing time approached, the ewes would be brought into the yards each night and received hay along with turnips or mangolds, while those with twins were given cake or crushed oats. Ram lambs were castrated at 10–14 days old, when all the lambs were tailed. Lamb-creeps encouraged the lambs at 3–4 weeks old to run ahead of their mothers folded on young turnip greens, the young being lured forward by troughs of finely ground cake and pea chaff. By early April ewes and lambs were being folded on rye, winter barley and winter oats, with mangolds for the ewes and cake for the lambs.

In May the ewes were at last out on the Downs again, for half the day at first, returning by 2.30 in the afternoon to the lambs folded on trifolium and ryegrass. Later in May the lambs were crib-fed on cut vetches and winter oats and by June the sheep had access to clover-ley aftermaths. The shepherd would be alert for fly attack at that time of year and would rub affected areas with diluted disinfectant after the sheep had been dagged.

In the first or second week of June the ewes were washed in running water in preparation for shearing a fortnight later, once the yolk or grease had risen in the fleece. Shearing took place in a sheltered yard or 'Down barn' with a cleanly swept floor to avoid dirtying the fleece. After shearing the ewes were kept for a night or two in a very sheltered fold until they were 'acclimatised to the loss of their jackets': even in June the Downs could produce sudden cold, damp fogs or chilly breezes.

The lambs were weaned during June and went on to a sainfoin ley or Dutch clover aftermath, with an extra ration of concentrates to compensate for the lack of milk. The ewes were taken to the far end of the farm, well out of sight and sound of their young, and spent the day on the

Downs, folding at night on aftermath or rape. By the end of the month they had been dipped 'in the permanent concrete swim-bath in vogue on most hill farms'.

Now came the time to 'make up' the flock. Older ewes were drafted and young ones who had some defect, or were not true to type, or had proved a disappointment in the lambing yard, were culled, their places being taken by the two-tooths. Draft ewes were given a little better 'doing' than the rest of the flock in order to prepare them for the August shows and sales, while the main flock continued to run on the Downs by day and be folded on aftermaths or rye stubbles at night.

Lambs were culled at the beginning of August, the best ewe lambs being kept to reinforce the flock in due course and the rest either run along as tegs or pushed ahead to fatten quickly on clover aftermath, cabbage, rape and kale. August was the dipping month for lambs, which were trimmed and dagged if necessary.

August was also the month for sire selection at the big ram sales, where flockmasters would look for well-bred rams from known ram-breeding flocks, choosing those with a good fleece, back length and shoulders, and with legs of mutton well let down. The draft ewes and culls would be disposed of and the new sheep year was about to begin all over again in September.

On a low-lying arable farm on what was described as a 'heavy 2-horse loam soil', it seems that the Southdown, though a natural grazer, adapted well to all-year folding on clover leys, wheat stubbles, rape, white turnips, swedes ('judiciously fed'), Dutch clover and trefoil, according to the season, with supplements of hay, and concentrates in limited quantities for mothers of twins and for lambs, with never more than half a pound per lamb.

On this lowland farm the rams were turned out with the ewes in September at the rate of eight to every three or four hundred. Lambing started in January. The ewes in the lambing-yard had free access to a trough of water and Epsom salts: 'If any of the ewes are feverish they will drink, and by this natural medicine will eliminate the chance of fever after lambing.'

The lambs were tailed and males castrated (except those saved for breeding) in January and weaned in June. June was also the month when the ewes were thoroughly washed, and they were washed again a fortnight after being shorn. In July the ewe lambs were culled and those saved for the ewe flock were put to the ram in October, when they were about nine months old.

On the light, arable lands of Cambridgeshire, close folding of Southdowns was highly recommended. A flock of 400 ewes was folded on 30 acres in rotation: sainfoin aftermath, ryegrass and clover, or rape and mustard, and subsequently stubble, kale, white turnips and so on. The ewes were put to the ram in the last week of August. The breeding system in this instance was very selective and labour intensive: the ewes were divided into small groups, each with its own ram, carefully chosen on the basis of relationships, fault-correcting etc. The ewes were monitored weekly to see if (and if so, why) any had turned and to ensure that each ewe came into the lambing-yard at the right time so that none would drop its lambs out in the field unnoticed, risking the loss of the young. During pregnancy, it was considerd that exercise was most important, especially in the six weeks immediately before lambing. They did not, of course, have the advantage of walking the Downs during the day.

The lambing period ran from mid-January to mid-February. The lambing-yard was a temporary or movable affair (for health reasons) built of rough posts and rails thatched with wheat straw and well littered with barley straw. The best possible food was stocked close to hand: cabbage, crushed oats, hay, mangolds and swedes.

Weaning took place as June matured into July and immediately after this the ewes were made to 'work hard for their living in order to get the milk down', generally on forty acres of very light heath land sown with lucerne. They were got up into better condition from about three weeks before the tup.

These basic routines were still practised in the mid-1940s. The best ewe lambs were selected in September; culls were either kept on for sale as stores in the autumn or as fat in early spring, or to sell as shearlings at the summer shows and sales. Sheep-washing was less prevalent, though the ewes would be dagged and trimmed at the britch before shearing at the end of May or beginning of June. By now the work was usually by machine rather than hand-shearing. Full-mouth regular draft ewes were picked out at this time and all other ewes inspected and culled for faults such as bad wool, poor udders, or a lack of colour or breed characteristics. Ram lambs for breeding and wether lambs being fattened for the butcher received the best of everything at all stages.

OPPORTUNITIES FOR SOUTHDOWNS TODAY

The main role of the Southdown will no doubt continue to be as a terminal sire for prime lamb and for crossbred lambs from ewe hoggs in their first breeding season, but there are less obvious outlets which deserve consideration in these changing times — some of them for profit, others for more altruistic reasons or for personal interest. One of the blessings of the Southdown is that it is of such quality and repute that it can be kept on a sound commercial basis by those attuned to its needs but it is also amenable enough to be kept for pleasure. Its gentleness and placidity can be exploited by those who have a little imagination.

Here, then, are some of the possibilities which can stand alone or be combined for successful enterprises on any scale. The list is not comprehensive but might serve as inspiration.

- Purebred rams as terminal sires
  (a) for prime lamb from commercial ewes, and
  (b) for bonus lambs from commercial ewe hoggs
  (c) for increasing productivity of smaller rare-breed ewes.
- High-class pedigree breeding stock for sale or export as sires or replacement ewes, with surplus lambs for meat. Use of pedigree flock-pooling to form good nucleus of breeding ewes for production of superior rams, including use of AI and embryo transplants to increase rate of improvement.
- Economic, easily managed and complementary secondary enterprise for dairy farmers.
- Exploitation of the pure lamb's carcase qualities by selling direct to specialist butchers and consumers (for example, hotels and restaurants) or for home use, fresh or frozen.
- Special emphasis on breeding and managing for wool, for sale to British Wool Marketing Board or privately to hand-spinners, or on-farm added-value products such as spun and dyed knitting yarns, knitted goods, sheepskin items.
- Land improvement — sward control; arable manuring by folding; orchard, paddock and graveyard grazing; ecological restoration and maintenance.
- Exhibition — at the shows or in farm parks (good docility for contact with the public), heritage collections (as basis for displays of

traditional agricultural practices and crafts), city farms (to encourage urban understanding of agriculture).

- Youth groups — encouraging an interest in sheep in general and the Southdown in particular, as a subject on the school curriculum, arranging farm visits for school parties (e.g. at lambing), initiating school and college flocks, setting up junior Southdown clubs, teaching show techniques — plenty of ideas from the United States.

FACTS FOR FARMERS

- EASY TO MANAGE
- EARLY MATURING
- PRIME MEAT
- MORE FOR LESS AND MORE QUICKLY

As a terminal sire

The Southdown's main role today is as a terminal sire for prime lamb from crossbred ewes, and particularly as a sire on ewe lambs or hoggets.

The Southdown's long history as a pure breed gives it a prepotency that guarantees that the ram's excellent carcase qualities are stamped on its progeny.

During the ewe's pregnancy, the lambs are small enough not to make heavy demands upon her — a particularly valuable factor for young ewes still growing. The lamb's tapered head and tidy shoulders ensure easy lambing in young ewes of any breed, and its ingrained Southdown determination to be up quickly and thrive is an added bonus. Nor is the lamb greedy for milk: it is easily satisfied, and a contented lamb reassures the ewe and gives her more time for grazing so that she can recover her resources rapidly and soon fills out for tupping or for sale. In addition, the lambs grow and mature quickly, further reducing pressure on the ewe and also giving the farmer quick returns. A pure Southdown lamb, for example, can finish off good grass in fourteen weeks.

Top quality carcase

The Southdown today is bigger and more rugged than it was forty years ago but it is still beautifully proportioned. It has retained its famous conformation for prime lamb: the loin is wide and flat, with thick, even fleshing down the legs, almost to the hocks. There is very little waste: the bones are small, the shank and neck are short, and butchers have always appreciated the Southdown as an exceptionally good cutter — 'chop chop, bang bang, and the job's done,' with very little wasted.

The meat has always been renowned for its excellent flavour and succulence, whether as lamb or as leg of mutton, and the small joints are particularly attractive to the discerning consumer. The Southdown name on the menu is traditionally appreciated and attractive. For smallholders, the small joints are ideal for the family and for the freezer.

Although the smallest of the Down breeds, the Southdown's size is deceptive: it is bigger than it looks. The body is not camouflaged by a long staple (no fleecy deception!), the bones are small and the fleshing is solidly placed where it counts. It offers flesh rather than frame, and that means a more economical animal to feed and to butcher.

It is sometimes said that Southdowns become too fat. The breed is an early ripener and, like any breed, will grow too fat if not managed properly.

The average mature weight of a modern Southdown ewe is 59–68 kg (130–150 lb) and top pedigree rams can weigh more than 90 kg (200 lb).

The shepherd's sheep

The Southdown is exceptionally docile and easy to manage. Fencing costs are minimal and it is a thoroughly hardy breed, used to the open, windswept southern downlands and tolerant of a wide range of environments, climates and management systems.

It is well known for its thriftiness and its ability to withstand times of hardship: 'a patience of occasional short keep, and endurance of hard stocking scarcely surpassed by any other sheep', as it was put in the nineteenth century. Now, as then, it can be more tightly stocked than any other breed, partly because it is small, lightfooted and docile, and partly because it is able to make the best of available grazing and forage: it has very good conversion rates. Southdowns really proved their worth during the big droughts of 1976 and 1989: they tolerated the immediate shortages and were very quick to recover condition.

Southdowns for wool

The dense, fine fleece covers the whole body and there is no kemp or coloured fibres, except for traces of mouse on the face and legs. It is the finest of the British wools and attracts top price for quality, making up for any lack of quantity.

MEAT PRODUCTION

Early maturity and the flavour of its meat are two major and well-known characteristics of the Southdown. It used to be famous for its leg of mutton but in Britain today mutton is a forgotten dish and the onion sauce is looking for a new partner. However, Southdown lamb is food for the connoisseur and crossbred lamb sired by a Southdown is quick money in the pocket for the commercial sheep-farmer.

Southdown rams on commercial ewe hoggs

The Southdown-cross lamb from a commercial ewe hogg is a 'bonus' lamb compact enough for troublefree lambing, and the use of Southdown sires on immature ewes is likely to continue to be a major outlet for the breed.

In an article in *Country Life* (28 June 1979) devoted to the Southdown, John L. Jones wrote:

> In a roundabout way, the inflationary price escalation of the past few years has helped the revival of the Southdown as a crossing ram for prime lamb production. The past six years has seen the price of good-class yearling hybrid breeding sheep rise ... which has led to many traditional yearling purchasers at the autumn sales moving to the purchase of ewe lambs which are lambed in their first year. Just as many dairy farmers who calve their heifers at an early age use the compact Aberdeen Angus bull to sire the first calf in the young still-growing heifer, so many

flockmasters breeding from ewe lambs now use the compact Southdown
to produce lambs from the ewe hoggs in their first year. With these
immature sheep the even conformation of the bigger modern Southdown, with its neat hornless head, makes for trouble-free lambing.

The Southdown cross lambs are usually sold at 70–76 lb liveweight — a little lighter than lambs from hoggs by the bigger Down
breeds, but with the reduced risks at parturition and the easier shepherding, which is a major compensation in the production of what is virtually
the 'bonus' lamb. A number of telling arguments can be marshalled in
favour of lambing ewe hoggs. They have a lower initial cost. Well grown,
well fed and well managed — preferably as a separate flock — some
pure breeds, and especially hybrids like the Welsh Halfbred, can
produce 100% lambing in their first year. This means they show a
substantial capital appreciation by the shearling stage (over £20 on last
year's average prices), leave a 'bonus' lamb, and also, the value of a
fleece.

Prime crossbred lamb from Southdowns

The British sheep industry is on the threshold of major marketing and
technological innovations which will cause radical changes at every
level. The most immediate is the cut in variable premium from the
beginning of 1990 and the likely consequential change of emphasis
from the lamb to the ewe. In the last few months before that first 25%
cut, the national breeding flocks increased by 4% and exports rose, the
latter trend accelerating as the effects of the variable premium reduc-
tions were felt. At the beginning of 1990 the United Kingdom was the
world's second largest lamb exporter, with a trade of 76 000 tonnes per
annum (mostly to Europe), and the figure was expected to rise to
120 000 by 1993, especially to France and also to Belgium, Switzerland
and Germany, which demanded carcases weighing 16–20 kg. Italy and
Spain, however, wanted much lighter carcases and in 1989 only 3% of
the British lamb crop was in the under-12 kg category. The export of
British lamb to Spain doubled to 3823 tonnes from 1988 to 1989 and
there is a special demand at Christmas and Easter, when the Spanish
choose very small cuts for barbecuing: 85% of households in Spain eat
barbecued lamb at Easter.

Changes in EC slaughterhouse regulations due to come into force in
1992 are expected to lead to the closure of nearly half Britain's 900

abattoirs. Those that survive will be under great pressure to supply exactly what the market wants, and as David Turner (the Dingley flock) points out: 'By sensible management, suiting the known characteristics of the breed, excellent carcases can be produced, matching *exactly* the current demand for small, high-conformation lamb.'

The dominant market forces at present are the supermarkets and the export trade but there are also small specialist outlets for the Southdown. With the removal of the guarantee system, the butchers will be determining the prices and they will be demanding quality. Every producer would be well advised to take a more personal interest in the requirements of the butchers, who are the direct link with the consumers of sheepmeat. As terminal sires have the greatest single influence on the nation's lamb quality, siring almost 70% of all lambs slaughtered, commercial lamb producers are bound to demand high-performance terminal sires in the future, and the Southdowns will be ready.

The Meat and Livestock Commission is instrumental in encouraging commercial performance-testing programmes and from its own point of view the main emphasis will be on reducing fat in the terminal sire breeds, though many breeders disagree with this emphasis. It is, of course, the total amount and depth of lean meat available in the desirable cuts which will count in the long run, and lean, heavyweight lambs will be in demand. Perhaps Southdown breeders have some thinking to do, though it should be borne in mind that the consumer tends to have fickle tastes and there is always a danger that the race for leanness and size will have awkward consequences for the producers, such as increased lambing problems and overheads.

For some time now the MLC has concentrated on the fat issue, to such an extent that the only published studies in which Southdowns are compared with other breeds seem to have been established in order to estimate the proportion of subcutaneous fat in crossbred lambs. However, some of the tables produced during these studies, though they tend to find the Southdown's fat proportions are high, throw interesting light on other factors which are worth further investigation.

For example, two five-year MLC studies published in *Animal Production* in 1987 (no. 44) analysed the growth and carcase characteristics of crossbred lambs by ten different sire breeds: Border Leicester, Dorset Down, Hampshire Down, Ile de France, North Country Cheviot, Oxford Down, Southdown, Suffolk, Texel and Wensleydale. The commercial flocks included Scottish Blackface, Scottish Halfbred and Mule ewes in a range of geographical regions and production systems. The progeny were slaughtered at what was estimated to be the same level of subcutaneous fat in the carcase. With regard to lambs sired by the Southdown, the following points were particularly noted.

The Southdown-cross lambs were in the 'small' category (i.e. with an estimated adult body size of 33–42 kg liveweight) but, although their carcases weights were the lowest, their daily carcase weight gains were the highest and, while the proportion of fat in the carcase was highest from Southdown sires (but by only a few grams per kilogram) the daily gain of *lean* tissue was top rate. (Incidentally, it is probably the ability to store a little extra fat that keeps the Southdown hardy and enables it to thrive in times of poor feeding, and carries the ewe in good condition during the stress of lamb-rearing.)

On a fifteen-point scale for carcase conformation, the Southdown crosses averaged the top rate (8.7) over all other combinations. Compared with other breeds, the Southdown-sired lamb scored very well indeed for lean:bone ratio and perhaps surprisingly well for

Newly shorn Welsh half-bred ewe hoggs with Southdown-cross lambs.
(*John L. Jones*)

lean:fat ratio in which it was third overall. But perhaps the most welcome result was in the analysis of the distribution of lean meat in the higher priced cuts (leg, chump, loin and best end neck): in the early flocks Southdown crosses were equal second best and in the late flocks they were third.

Production efficiency

More than a century ago, in 1861/62, members of the Partington Tenants' Club in Yorkshire decided to measure the production efficiency of various sheep breeds in relation to profitability. Lawrence Alderson, in his book *The Chance to Survive*, reproduced the results: the Southdown, among the smallest breeds of the time at a carcase weight of 51 kg (compared with the 49 kg Cotswold, the 52 kg North sheep and the 54 kg Teeswater cross among others) was by far the cheapest to feed of all the seven breeds tested. It had a more valuable carcase and higher overall profit margin than the other small-carcase breeds, in spite of its wool yield being by far the lowest of all the breeds and thus worth only two-fifths that of the top-yielding wool breed, the Lincoln, which also won handsomely on carcase weight, but was by far the most expensive to feed. The value of the experiment was to highlight the fact that output needs to be related to input if figures are to be meaningful, and the Southdown is a thrifty breed in this respect.

How it grows

For newcomers to meat production, it is worth considering how animals develop the different types of body tissue as they grow. Any overall weight increase is shared by the various tissues and body parts but in different proportions at different stages. To make best use of the information which follows, it is important to *weigh* stock regularly — on the scales and not just by eye, even if you are an expert.

In early life the rate of overall weight gain is fairly constant for the first month or so but a lamb begins to grow faster from the age of perhaps six or seven weeks old and maintains a higher growth rate until it approaches carcase maturity — an age which varies according to the breed.

The ewe, as it happens, is not a very efficient converter of her food into milk compared with a cow, nor is a sheep very efficient in converting its food into meat. As an animal grows and gains weight, its food conversion efficiency decreases: a lamb with a liveweight of, say, 10 kg, needs about 1.5 kg of food just for maintenance and an extra kilo of food for every kilo of liveweight gain, while a lamb three times that weight needs about 3.5 kg for maintenance and perhaps 1.5 kg for each kilo of liveweight gain. There naturally comes a point when the animal is more profitably slaughtered than continuing to be fed, and the younger it reaches a reasonable slaughterweight, the better.

In general, the faster it grows, the more efficient its food conversion, but the bigger breeds need a greater weight of food for maintenance and a balance must be struck: bigger it not necessarily better. The more it weighs, the more it eats, and the economic trick is to balance the cost of inputs against the price per kilo of edible carcase. Inputs include more than food: the heavier types generally stay longer on the farm, which can cost in terms of use of buildings and other outgoings as well as perhaps being inconvenient.

Much of the early growth is in building up the skeletal structure and internal organs, especially in vascular and digestive systems. The skeleton develops in recognisable stages and the changing proportions are easy to notice. Next comes a phase of muscle development over the skeleton — and muscle, of course, is lean meat. After the main development of the muscles, different types of fat begin to be deposited at an increasing rate to fill out the animal's body, and they are deposited at an earlier stage if nutrition intake exceeds the energy needed to lay down bone and muscle. The order in which different types of body fat are laid down is, first, the kidney knob and channel fat (KKCF), then the deposits between the muscles, the subcutaneous fat under the skin, and finally the intramuscular fat or marbling which gives such succulence to top quality meat.

The proportions of these body tissues, as each type reaches its prime growth stage, obviously alter with time in relation to each other. Initially the proportion of bone is very high; the proportion of lean tends to remain fairly constant up to slaughterweight and then begins to fall as the proportion of fat rapidly increases. The perfect slaughterweight is when lean is at its maximum and before the proportion of fat in comparison to lean has become unacceptable. Once the stage of major fat deposition has been reached (i.e. carcase maturity) any excess nutrition will add to fat rather than to lean.

If ill health, a poor environment or malnutrition are experienced during the various growth phases, they will check that stage of development: in early life, for example, skeletal stunting might occur and the animal will always be smaller than it should be. Muscular development will also be reduced because of the small frame and the tendency will be for the animal to put on fat at an earlier stage if it is subsequently well fed, so that at slaughter what looked like a prime lamb on the hoof will have far too high a proportion of fat to lean on the hook.

Early maturing animals develop their skeletons rapidly, growing short, thick, round bones over which the muscles will be deep and short and will also develop quickly, so that the animal is ready to deposit fat at a relatively light weight and early age. Later maturing animals have longer, more slender bones, longer and shallower muscles, and delayed fat deposition: they are ready for slaughter at a later age and heavier weight.

The adult liveweight of a breed gives an indication of the best slaughterweights for carcases within the most acceptable classes, as long as the adult weight is that for the breed rather than for a particular flock or farm, since on-farm environments and management systems create wide variations within a breed. The accepted breed liveweights are the average of mature ram and ewe weights and at present that for the purebred Southdown is 61 kg, according to the MLC. The potential adult breed liveweight of a crossbred lamb lies midway between the breed weights of its parents, which will give a reliable guide to the average fat class of batches of lambs if not of individuals.

The standard formula is that lambs that have grown well without a check and are slaughtered at *half their potential adult breed liveweight* will kill out at about 48% and produce carcases in fat class 3. As a general guide, lambs slaughtered at about 10% below the predicted slaughter-weight for a breed or cross will usually produce carcases of fat class 2, so that leaner lambs can be attained either by selling the same type of lamb at a lighter weight or by selling at the same weight but using a combination of larger breed types. The sex of the lamb makes a difference as well: ewe lambs are fatter than wether lambs of the same breed at the same weight, and to achieve the same fat class wethers should be killed at 5% above the average slaughterweight and ewe lambs at 10% below it. Also, winter lambs can usually be taken to slightly heavier weights than lambs finished off grass but still remain in the same fat class (say 5% heavier) as they tend to grow more slowly.

All these figures are for guidance only, of course, and apply to batches rather than individuals. To meet market demands it is important to weigh each lamb regularly and become practised at assessing its level of fatness at the main handling points — especially around the tail root and along the backbone. It is not an art that can be taught but it is gained with experience.

The MLC grading scheme for lamb describes carcases in terms of two main factors: fatness and conformation The fat classes range from 1 (very lean) to 5 (very fat), with classes 3 and 4 being divided into L (lower) and H (higher). The current demand is for lamb in fat class 2 or 3L: in class 2 the fat cover is thin, individual bones at the tail root are easily detectable with light fingertip pressure and along the backbone the spinous processes are prominent and easily felt individually, while in class 3 the individual bones around the tail root can be detected with light pressure, but not so easily, while the spinous processes have rounded tips and the individual bones can be felt as corrugations. If you need firm fingertip pressure to detect individual bones around the tail root, the fat cover is quite thick and the lamb is in class 4. Those in fat classes 4H and 5 or conformation class P have not been eligible for the variable premium since 1986. Variable premiums also took into account the carcase weight and the category of the animal.

The top conformation grade is E and the carcases which attract premiums from butchers are usually in categories 2E or 3E (the fat class being given first) though conformation class U is also acceptable. (The conformation classes, in descending order, reflect Britain's membership of the EC: they are E, U, R, O and P.) An average carcase — not too bad but not the best — would be conformation class R, fat class 3L.

From the butcher's point of view, the fat class affects the percentage of saleable meat in the carcase weight once excess fat has been trimmed away, and also the proportions of lean, fat and bone in the carcase. Subcutaneous fat is easily trimmed from the carcase, of course, but even in boned carcases it is difficult for the butcher to remove intermuscular fat, and until the consumer wants fat on the plate, the butcher wants less fat in the carcase.

The thickness of the meat is determined largely by breeding, with very little effect from flock management: hill breeds, for example, tend to have angular, leggy conformation but this can be improved by the use of carefully selected rams of blocky conformation from meat sire breeds, which will help produce a higher proportion of lambs with better conformation. This is where the Southdown comes into its own: its conformation is famous for its top quality, whether in the purebred or passed to a Southdown ram's crossbred offspring.

Any Southdown breeder will recognise that the breed falls firmly into the early-maturing category; indeed, it is the earliest of all British breeds, so that a pure Southdown is at its prime for slaughter when it is very young and therefore still quite lightweight. It will soon start to be far too fat for modern tastes and inefficient at food conversion during subsequent weight gain, as it takes much more energy to create a pound of fat than a pound of muscle. A Southdown cross is also early-maturing and will become too fat if kept too long in the hope of greater slaughterweights but in both cases, if slaughtered at the right point, the carcases will fetch premiums for quality and will usually grade very economically off grass. For example, Southdowns on Scottish Halfbreds will readily produce acceptably lean and gradable lambs of 17–18 kg.

The Southdown sire's qualities of early maturity and rapid growth make it ideal for those aiming at the early lamb market, bearing in mind that peak lamb prices are usually obtained some time around Easter, but it is important to choose a good strain *within the breed*: some strains become too fat sooner than others.

WOOL PRODUCTION

Traditionally, wool was the sheep farmer's main source of income, but today it accounts for only perhaps between 10 and 20% of the gross returns per ewe. The major factor in wool grading is *fineness*, measured in terms of the 'Bradford Count' quality numbers, which indicate the number of hanks of yarn 510 m long that can be spun from 450 g of wool (or 560 yards long from one pound): the higher the count, the finer the wool.

The finer wool fibres are produced by secondary follicles on the skin which are associated with sebaceous glands, while the coarser hair or kemp fibres are produced by primary follicles associated with erector muscles and sweat glands. The higher the proportion of secondary to primary follicles in a breed, the finer its fleece. Most British breeds have a ratio of perhaps eight secondary follicles to every primary and the British wools generally range in quality from 28s to 58s, but the Merino's ratio is as high as 25 to 1, with a Bradford Count of at least 80. The Southdown, at 56s to 60s, gives the finest wool in Britain along with the Ryeland. Except in the Merino, fleeces are not usually uniform and in most cases the finest wool is on the shoulder while the coarsest is in the britch.

Another factor is the wool's *crimp*, which is reflected by the number of corrugations in a 25 mm length of fibre. Crimp is closely associated with fineness and varies from 8 to 28. A combination of a high degree of crimp with a fairly thick fibre diameter gives British wool its typical springiness and elasticity.

A third factor is the *length of the staple*, which obviously has a direct effect on the total fleece weight. A longwool like the Teeswater can produce perhaps 5 to 6 kg, a Swaledale on the hills only 2 kg, and the Southdown perhaps 1.5–2.25 kg. The Southdown's staple length of 40–60 mm is about the shortest in Britain, bar the almost naked Wiltshire Horn (5 mm) and some individuals in the North Ronaldsay (40–80 mm). In general, the longer the fibres, the thicker.

Apart from breeding, fleece quality is affected by the general environment and by nutrition. Regions where the land and the rainfall are light are generally quite unsuitable for coarse-woolled sheep (who would fail to develop their potential fleece weight and staple length) but are better for fine-woolled sheep who, conversely, do not produce such good fleeces in wet conditions. Here the wool becomes discoloured and loses 'style', which is the external appearance or condition of a shorn fleece when it is first examined.

Wool growth is essentially cyclical and photoperiodic (i.e. it relates to daylength) and in Britain 80% of wool growth occurs between July and November. It continues to grow even if nutrition levels are such that the sheep's energy balance is thrown into the negative; but in that case it grows more slowly and becomes finer, so that the final clip will be lighter in weight. Underfeeding also produces 'tenderness' in the wool: a thinner area develops at a point along the fibre corresponding to the period of low nutrition and the check not only gives an undesirable lack of uniformity to the fibre but can even prompt premature shedding. Tender wools can also result from illness or a period of drought and it is possible to see a break in all the fibres at one point in the staple reflecting the 'traumatic' period. Those who value their wool crop should take extra care that ewes suckling more than one lamb are not too heavily drawn upon and should take special precautions to deal with internal parasites which would further drain the ewe's resources.

Although only about 14% of wool growth occurs from December to February in Britain, ewe management during the winter is crucial to fleece quality. The final weeks of pregnancy and the early suckling period are critical and the results of a difficult environment at this stage often show up as cotting and breaking in the fleece at shearing time. They are not necessarily avoided by correct and palatable feeding, though the latter will certainly help.

At any stage, stocking rates which are so heavy that feed shortages result at critical times inevitably reduce the weight and value of the fleece.

Naturally great care needs to be taken at shearing so that fleeces are not ruined by double cutting (which reduces staple length), contamination or poor presentation. Many a fleece is presented unwrapped, or badly wrapped, or contaminated with vegetable matter, woodshavings or dung, or has been badly stored or contains coloured fibres. Careless contamination often occurs on the shearing floor or at the time of wrapping: those who use wool sheets, for example, should not lace them with polypropylene or indeed any other twine or string except the special twine supplied by some merchants. Considerable penalties can be levied for artificial staining and discoloration, the presence of branding contaminants, failure to roll the fleece, fleeces tied with twine or cord, and claggy or undagged fleeces.

The approved method of fleece presentation is this. After shearing, place the fleece flesh-side down on a clean surface. Remove any daggs and pick off extraneous matter. Include only clean, dry belly wool with the fleece before folding in the flanks towards the centre. Then turn in the britch end and roll the fleece firmly, and neatly, toward the neck. After rolling, part the fleece and, without twisting, tuck the neck wool firmly into the body of the parted fleece, then place the tucked fleece firmly into the wool sheet.

The Southdown's fine, soft, crimply wool compensates in quality for its lack of quantity, which is typical of the breed in all respects. There is no kemp or colour in it. Typical greasy fleece weights are 2–3 kg for

ewes, 2.3–3.6 kg for tegs and 3.2–5.5 kg for rams, though the BWMB
suggests that the average Southdown fleece yield is 1.5–2.25 kg (the
yield being the amount of clean, dry wool remaining after dirt and
grease have been commercially scoured from the fleece) with a staple
length of 40–60 mm, and quality in the range of 56s–60s. The wool is
used for a wide range of high quality fabrics such as hosiery, dress
fabrics, flannel, light tweeds and also yarns for hand-knitting, and is
ideal for lightweight underwear because of its softness, elasticity and
insulation properties. It is, of course, placed in the Shortwool and
Down classification and it heads that group as the only breed whose
wool is officially described by BWMB as 'Very Fine'. The full wool
grade specification for Southdowns in England, Wales and Scotland is:

Grade	104
Degree of fineness:	Very fine, 58/60s
Length of staple:	Short, 1–2 inches, uniform
Handle of wool:	Soft
Degree of lustre:	None
Colour:	Creamy
Strength:	Sound
Other factors:	Free of kemp and grey fibres

Indeed BWMB remarked on the Southdown in 1989: 'The only
immediate problem that springs to mind is its scarcity. In the 1988
season we produced less than 3000 kg greasy fleece wool, and in many
eyes it is now fast becoming a rare breed.' It is interesting to note that
the medium-wool piebald Jacob, once an official rare breed, whose
fortunes were radically changed by an excellent co-ordinated marketing programme a few years ago, produced a total clip of 78 000 kg in
1988.

Incidentally, the Board offers any wool producer a free ram-fleece
assessment service to help producers throughout the UK to improve
wool quality and fleece weights. It also runs national shearing courses
and offers plenty of advice on management for wool production.

The Southdown has certainly improved its clip over the decades. In
1800 the average Southdown fleece weight was only a couple of pounds
(less than a kilo) with a staple of $1\frac{1}{2}$ inches on the hills, but during the
nineteenth century it increased to 3 lb and 2 inches, while on the
lowlands it rose from 3 lb to $3\frac{1}{2}$ or 4 lb, with a 4-inch staple, partly
because the lowland was a larger type of sheep and partly because of its

feeding. It was noted in the nineteenth century that 'the colour of the wool differs materially according to the colour of the soil. The shortest and finest wool is produced on the chalky soil, where the sheep have to travel far for their food; but there is a harshness and brittleness about this wool which was always seriously objected to.' Apparently wool from the Downs flocks was originally used principally in the manufacture of 'servants' and army clothing' but later in the century, when the fibre had materially increased in length, it became a combing wool instead of an inferior carding one and it contributed to 'flannels, baizes and worsted goods of almost every description — its fineness and its felting, compared with some of the other short wools, renders it a truly valuable article.' Hogget wool, untouched until the second shearing, had apparently always been a combing wool and was finer than long wool.

Lord Somerville, in a letter to John Ellman, said:

> Your South Downs must be cotted in the winter, or the wool will not work mellow enough for fine cloths; so the manufacturers say. Your sample of wool, I find, is superior to anything they have seen, or could believe. To you I look for the example of cotting all your wool next winter. In three years your staple would be more than one-fifth finer. The hard keep Ryeland sheep will bear, when cotted at an easy expense, cries out for universal imitation.

By 1922 it was proposed (by Professor J. Cossar Ewart of Edinburgh University) that Down wools were a cross between mountain sheep and Merino in type and combined mountain crispness and fullness with typical Merino fineness, curliness, waviness and softness. If Down wools were badly grown, however, they lost uniformity and fullness of staple and the softness and fineness of the fibre, and to avoid such problems the Southdown Sheep Society suggested some golden rules. But be warned that these rules are not considered so golden today — their fallacies are discussed later.

- Uniformity of feed to ensure uniformity of fibre and staple.
- Protection from really inclement weather.
- Suitable pasturage of such a character that, at least for some time before shearing, the wool on the sheep's back is got into and is maintained in good condition, free of soil and of all vegetable contamination.

On the traditional practice of wool-washing before shearing, the Society explained that, as a fine wool, the Southdown's fleece was heavy and rich in yolk but that fine wools were better judged in the full greasy state. An average Southdown greasy wool had proportions of 55% wool to 45% yolk etc., while the washed wool's proportions were 70:30. There had been some thought given to the possibility of washing the sheep in tanks (rather than in running streams on the Downs) so that the lanoline and potash salts could be reclaimed but this was deemed too costly. If the sheep *were* washed, it was suggested that there should be a lapse of twelve days before shearing in order to enable the yolk to rise in the staple and give the wool softness and plasticity.

It was admitted that short-fibred fleeces were quite difficult to 'get up' by self-binding but, even in the 1920s, the use of any kind of string to secure the fleece was known to contaminate the wool and it was suggested that paper bands might be used instead.

At this period, Southdown wool was the finest in diameter of all British wools at 1/800 to 1/900 of an inch, with an average staple length of 3 inches; the only shorter wool was that of the primitive Soay. However, the Southdown's was quite long enough for combing and it was deemed important not to gain staple length at the expense of density and 'squareness' of the staple form (which indicated regularity in the fibres). It was said that the fleece had 'a certain creamy-lustre appearance' somewhere between the lustre of a Wensleydale and the opacity of a Merino. In terms of crimp, the finest Merino wool had 36 waves per inch, the Southdown 14, the Oxford Down 8–10 and the Lincoln little or none.

It was felt that the Southdown, like the Merino, produced its finest wool on 'pasturage upon which heavier sheep would starve' and an experimental cross of Southdown on indigenous Merino ewes pastured several thousand feet up in the Peruvian Andes had produced wool of 'quite extraordinary value'. The pure Southdowns and their crossbred lambs both appeared to thrive under these extreme conditions, an observation which put paid once and for all to the aspersion that the Southdowns were not as hardy as they might be. In Britain, meanwhile, Merino and Down wools were frequently blended anyway.

Looking to the future — the distant future — research is in hand in Australian biotechnology laboratories to implant genes into sheep in order to boost wool growth and improve its quality. Genes are transplanted from bacteria and these 'transgenic' sheep will have digestive systems modified to make available a higher amount of the nutrients needed for wool growth and will be able to make cysteine, a wool-growing nutrient which is a vital ingredient of the keratin proteins that form the core of wool fibres. Experiments are now being carried out to see if these gene transplantations will in fact successfully increase the supply of cysteine to the wool follicles and apparently the Australians have so far produced a woolly transgenic mouse (!) carrying a sheep gene. Eventually they hope to transfer the mouse's wool-growing ability to real sheep and to control the type and quality of the fleece, enhancing the dye-penetration properties and improving the fibres' resistance to abrasion. Once the biotechnologists begin tinkering with sheep genes, there is no knowing what the future holds.

To return to the present, at a more practical level for today's wool producers, Peter Clementson has several tips for Southdown flock masters interested in wool quality. The traditional type of Southdown produces its best wool on harder keep, as long as the sheep have adequate nutrition to maintain their general condition and to meet the challenge of lambing. The important rule is to keep them *steady*: put them on tight grazing all year round, with not more than a couple of inches of grass. Uniformity of keep leads to the desirable uniformity of staple, but they should not be overfed. Too much food will no doubt increase their general size and carcase weight but it ruins the wool quality, losing the characteristic short staple and great density of the fleece. The sheep are being pushed beyond their proper potential and the wool grows longer and coarser.

It has already been explained that variations in keep lead to variations in fibre thickness and this became particularly evident in 1976 and 1989 when major droughts resulted in a severe shortage of grazing. The Southdowns, being so thrifty, did better than most breeds to regain condition later in the year but the fleece fibres could be read like a tree's growth rings and reflected the time of extreme hardness in a noticeable reduction of fibre thickness corresponding with the drought period, which contrasted with the thicker diameter produced by putting the ewes on corn for lambing.

Clementson's sheep are always on hard keep in Kent: the grazing is rough permanent 'pasture' over terrain which includes old rubbish-tip fill-ins and old gravel pits. They also face fairly rough weather, contending with winds all year round, and their excellent fleece quality in such conditions completely repudiates the Society's 1922 'golden

Mr Peter Clementson and two of his Southdowns with Lady Bidwell (Lady Mayoress of London, and a descendent of Jonas Webb) at the Royal Smithfield Show, 1989. (*By kind permission of the Royal Smithfield Club*)

rule' of protecting the flock from inclement weather. Clementson also disagrees with the emphasis of the third rule: he points out that fleeces are much more likely to become contaminated in winter than in the few weeks before shearing, and the aim must be to keep the wool clean in the vulnerable period after shearing by keeping the flock on very short grass and then ensuring that, during the critical winter period, hay contamination is avoided by feeding the hay on the ground, not from racks from which the material will shower down on the fleece. The new golden rules for wool production are:

- Careful choice of breeding stock of the traditional type
- A harder keep for better quality wool
- Steady keep for uniformity of staple
- A sequence of very short sward in summer and ground-fed hay in winter to avoid fleece contamination

Peter Clementson's fleeces are international prize-winners and his advice must be well worth heeding.

ECOLOGY

The very ecology of the South Downs depended on a careful balance between the herbivores — sheep and rabbits — which gave the turf its distinctive character, kept down invasive scrub and created a perfect environment for the herbs, birds and butterflies that are still associated with the chalk downs, if only in memory. The poor quality of downland soil actually encourages a great richness in wild flowers and their associated insects: it is still possible to find up to forty different plants in a square metre of unspoilt downland turf but the turf itself is quickly disappearing.

The combination of myxomatosis among rabbits and the decline in sheep numbers has radically altered the intricate ecological structure on some parts of the South Downs in the past three or four decades, and a great increase in human leisure activities poses even more of a threat to the downland we remember from childhood. Worse still, the conservation officer of West Sussex County Council remarked in 1990 that he was also fighting a losing battle with the plough, although the whole of the South Downs from Beachy Head to Winchester was

Shepherd Waymark watering his flock at a dew pond at New House Farm (now farmed by Mr David Humphrey), East Dean, West Sussex. Man-made dew ponds were the main source of drinking water for sheep on the chalk Downs; usually circular, they were lined with straw and puddled clay and they collected rainwater or condensed mist. (*British Wool Marketing Board*)

designated as an environmentally sensitive area in 1987. Under a five-year scheme, farmers were given financial incentives to graze the Downs without using fertilisers or pesticides and were paid if they undertook to revert to grassland. However, although about half of the three hundred Downs farmers and landowners received payments under the scheme, only about 12% of the 150 000 acres within the designated area were covered by conservation agreements and it was strongly suspected that many farmers anyway intended to plough up reverted grassland as soon as their five-year agreements ended in 1991. Once ploughed, of course, the true downland turf is probably lost to future generations.

There is certainly a role for the Southdown today in restoring what is left of its native environment or, as Paul Wakeham-Dawson described it in *The Ark* (published by the Rare Breeds Survival Trust), 'preserving the past for the future' by using an appropriate regional breed to develop important ecological sites.

In response to Wakeham-Dawson's suggestion in *The Ark*, Elizabeth Henson of the Cotswold Farm Park described the use of Cotswold sheep to restore the ancient grassland on Cranham Common. A major problem in the early stages had been the rules against fencing common-land and the flock has now been trained not to stray, with the help of the Nature Conservancy Council and a control system developed in the United States for restricting dogs to their own gardens. A wire is buried under the soil along the boundaries; the sheep wear radio-controlled collars around their necks which trigger a minor electric shock when the animal strays across the wire, which is 'flagged' so that the sheep quickly learn to avoid the boundary and their grazing is controlled! It would hardly be economical with a flock of any size but it has possibilities for small groups of Southdowns, especially as they are so amenable. Small areas such as graveyards, for example, could benefit, and indeed sheep from Hugh Clark's Moulton flock have been quietly mowing local graveyards for the last thirty years, and at least one vicar uses his own small flock of Southdowns for the same purpose.

But there is more to it than mowing, scenery and wild flowers. Take by way of example a herbivore far removed from the Southdown: the feral goat. Goats are being used in some upland regions to improve the grazing for commercial sheep flocks by cleaning up the coarser vegetation, and they are simultaneously being exploited for fibre production by mating to selected billies for cashmere. Soon, if a market can be established, the feral goats will also be exploited for kid meat, so that an animal once ignored as useless or considered a pest is now potentially of both environmental and commercial value.

In the case of the Southdown restoring downland ecology, there is also the opportunity to produce fine wool from wether flocks. This practice could usefully be employed on set-aside land as well so that the land is maintained in good heart for the future through grazing and manuring while a small cash crop is generated almost by the way. With the likelihood of strictures on the use of artificial fertilisers anyway, there might even be something of a return to the tradition of folding Southdowns on arable land to maintain its fertility: the Southdown was a 'green' sheep long before green became a fashionable colour, and the sheep was a natural recyclist of on-farm nutrients long before recycling became the wheels of a political bandwagon.

It might be almost too late to save the beauty and character of the South Downs and restore the rich diversity of life which used to thrive on carefully grazed downland turf but surely it is worth trying. There could be no more appropriate tool for the job than the Southdown sheep.

SHOWING

Showing is vital for the future of the breed. It is at shows that competing breeders can assess and compare their stock and where less experienced breeders can 'get their eye in' and learn about the finer points of the Southdown, asking questions of experienced exhibitors and judges, listening to comments, seeing the best and being inspired to aim for it. Shows are ideal meeting places for those with a common interest, where they can exchange stock, information and views formally or informally. Above all, shows and carcase competitions offer breeders the opportunity to bring the Southdown to the attention of those who have not yet appreciated its worth. Individual flockmasters might be exhibiting for personal prestige (and ultimately profit) but it is the breed as a whole that benefits from their successes. Southdown breeder Dr David Turner, flockmaster of the Dingley flock near Market Harborough in Leicestershire, has written an invaluable book, *The Showman Shepherd*, published in 1990, which is a detailed guide to preparing and showing sheep.

Showing has always been essential to breed promotion and great strides could be made if more Southdowns were entered in more classes at more shows to remind a much wider public of their merits. A few decades ago Southdowns were well known in show-rings all over the country; today, however, they tend to be restricted to more localised shows where they are already well enough known, and even then only a few sheep are entered. At present, except in those areas and at the Royal, the Southdown is not offered its own classes but is entered with 'Other Down Breeds' or 'Other Pure Breeds', and this lack of breed status is reflected in the less prominent penning arrangements at the shows, all of which belittles the breed. The main shows with Southdown classes today are the Royal, the Royal Welsh, the South of England, the Kent, the Royal Bath and West, the Royal Smithfield, Findon Fair and, more recently, the Rare Breeds Survival Trust's Show and Sale, which is becoming a particular focal point for the breed. There are also general classses at various county shows (for example, Surrey, Derby and Leicester) and regional shows such as the East of England, and numerous local shows all over the country. The rare breeds event at the Weald and Downland Open Air Museum, Singleton, is a natural arena for the native Downs breed of Sussex, of course.

Southdown breeders in Britain might like to take a few leads from their American counterparts, whose innovative activities are described in the US section. In particular, it would be as well to heed the American realisation that the young of today are the sheep-breeders and buyers of tomorrow. The Southdown is an ideal breed for the young: its size and gentleness make it so easy and satisfying to handle, whether in the field or in the ring, even if the handler is a small child.

Showing is a vital part of breed promotion, and promotion is essential to the Southdown's future. This book seeks to convey a sense of pride in the heritage passed down to today's flock masters by Ellman and his successors, and to pass their torches of expertise, imagination, flair and enthusiasm to a new generation. This new generation could carry the Southdown into its third century with a determination to restore it to its rightful place as one of the most influential breeds Britain has ever produced, and give this compact parcel of good qualities as a gift to the future.

MARKETING

Many of today's Southdown breeders, from larger commercial farmers to smallholders, responded to a 1989 survey about outlets for their stock. Half of them specified that they were selling breeding stock, a quarter were supplying meat markets of various kinds, and the remainder did not state the type of stock.

Nearly half the respondents sold stock privately, either by word of mouth or by advertising; the majority of the rest sold at shows or through markets, and a few sold fatstock direct to their local butcher, foregoing lamb premiums. The most popular public outlet for breeding stock was the RBST Show and Sale, though Findon Fair comes a fairly close second. Other fairs, shows and markets mentioned for breeding stock or fatstock included in particular Ashford and Lewes, with single mentions for Wilton, Canterbury, Kelso, Builth Wells, Castle Douglas, Orkney, Chelford and the Dolphin Sheep Fair.

Those interested in seeing or buying purebred Southdowns would find it valuable to attend any of the following main sales:

- FINDON GREAT FAIR, near Worthing, Sussex
  second Saturday in September
  Auctioneers: Handleys (04352 6688)
- RARE BREEDS SURVIVAL TRUST SHOW AND SALE,
  Stoneleigh, Warwickshire
  second Saturday in September
  Auctioneers: John Thornborrow (0926 29946)
- ASHFORD, Kent
  first three Thursdays in October
  Auctioneers: Hobbs Parker (0233 22222)
- WILTON, near Salisbury, Wiltshire
  second Thursday of August, September and October
  Auctioneers: Woolley & Wallis (0722 21711)
- KELSO, Berwickshire
  second Friday of September
  Auctioneers: Berwick Auction Mart Co. (0209 307408)

CHAPTER ELEVEN

Sheep Fairs

In John Ellman's time a fair was instituted at Selmeston, a small village
a few miles east of Lewes, and in 1793 there were about 8000 sheep
there but very few buyers. There was also the Toy Fair, originally held
on the clifftops of Brighthelmston (or Brighton, as it is today) between
Ship Street and Black Lion Street. As the town grew, so did the fair,
and it was transferred to Belle Vue field (now the site of Regency
Square) and then to the Level where the first Sheep Fair was held on 4
September 1807, in recognition of the rapid advances made in Sussex
agriculture since the turn of the century. In particular the fair
celebrated the local Southdown: the aim was 'to fix ... a spot where a
pure, unmixed breed shall always be produced, and where the pur-
chaser (who, perhaps, comes from a distance) shall be sure of unadul-
terated stock.' This was deemed to be especially valuable to those who
were interested in

> that useful and highly productive animal, the South Down Sheep. Those
> who possess this breed, true and genuine, have much reason to lament
> that at Fairs, where a great variety of sheep are brought to market, many
> are sold for South Down Sheep which have no pretension to be so called
> and which afterwards, not answering the purpose of the buyers, bring
> unmerited disgrace to such as are really genuine.

For that reason, a large group of well-known flock masters, breeders of
pure Southdowns, decided to establish their fair on Brighton Level and

pledged themselves to bring to it 'genuine South Down Tups, Stock Ewes, Ewe Lambs and Wether Lambs; and, moreover, we will not either ourselves introduce, or suffer to be introduced to this fair, any but what shall be of genuine and true South Down Breed.' That first year there were about 20 000 prime Southdowns sold at the fair, and the same the following year, but, sadly, this worthy fair lasted only four years in all.

In the Southdown's heyday, there were well-known Sussex lamb fairs at St John's Common and at Horsham, and major sheep fairs at Lewes and Lindfield as well as regional markets at Chichester, Pulborough and Steyning. The Lindfield Fair was originally held on 5 August but later changed to 8 August to avoid the August bank holiday. Lewes Sheep Fair was originally held on 2 October but in 1809 it changed to 21 September, partly because there were other fairs on the old date, especially at Croydon, but also because those who travelled long distances to buy ewes were unable to bring their purchases home in time to be put to the ram. In the nineteenth century, Lewes was the principal market for Southdown wool: there was a fortnightly stock-market, attended by woolstaplers, and the main wool fair took place on 26 July.

Arthur Young, in his monumental *General View of the Agriculture of the County of Sussex* published in 1813, said of the Lewes Sheep Fair: 'It is from hence that the Southdown flocks are dispersed over various quarters of England as the buyers come from great distance to attend Lewes upon this day where large droves are brought up by commission. From 20 000 to 30 000 sheep are generally collected upon this occasion.'

Above all, of course, there has always been the Southdown's special fair at Findon, though Young mentioned it only in passing by including its date in his calendar of fairs, along with those of many other Sussex sales which have since disappeared. In 1927 Barclay Wills went to Findon Fair on 14 September and saw 10 000 sheep and lambs for sale.

Opposite Findon Fair 1930: in the foreground are the writer Barclay Wills and William 'Old Shep' Shepherd (wearing his smock). This annual event on Nepcote Green is the largest sheep fair in Sussex; it has medieval origins and from the 1790s was traditionally held on 14 September but the date was changed in the late 1950s to the second Saturday in September. Findon Fair is one of the Society's official shows and sales and a major venue for Southdown breeders.

(George Garland Collection, West Sussex County Record Office)

There were roundabouts, coconut shies, refreshment tents, and sheep penned by hurdles as far as the eye could see along the length of Nepcote Green. The scene was photographed in the 1930s by George Garland and looked remarkably similar to the Fair as it is now, except that in the old days nearly all the sheep were Southdowns.

The origins of Findon Fair go back a very long way and there was probably an annual fair and weekly village market even before medieval times. Findon, a few miles north of Worthing, is at a point where many ancient downland tracks converge; it was in an area of prehistoric settlements and there is an Iron Age hill fort at Cissbury Ring not far from the village.

In 1261, during the reign of Henry III, a Charter was granted to Walter de Clifford, Lord of the Manor, for a weekly Tuesday market at Findon. The Charter included an annual three-day fair over the Decollation of St John the Baptist (29 August) but it lapsed over the centuries and by the mid-seventeenth century there was only an annual sale of 'pedlary' on Holy Thursday.

In more or less its present form, Findon's Great Sheep Fair was established above the village at Nepcote Green by George Holford some time after 1790. In those days there were huge numbers of sheep in Sussex, especially on the South Downs, and it was no doubt the pressing need to market them that revitalised existing fairs as suitable sales outlets. As Findon was a Charter fair, there were tolls to be collected by the Lord of the Manor, levied per score of sheep sold, and these manorial rights came to the Margesson family, who had purchased Findon Place. It appears that at some stage the family subcontracted their rights to the Holfords, who continued to manage the Fair for a century and a half after George Holford first established it at Nepcote Green. Holford's role was apparently to pitch the Fair, provide and repair the wattles and other tackle, erect the pens, allocate them to various vendors as they arrived, collect his tolls from the flock owners, put everything away again after the event and settle up with the Lord of the Manor, to whom he paid a small toll. Later Holford paid a rent for the brick-and-flint Wattle House purpose-built in 1803 to store the wattles on its ground floor (there were two cottage tenements upstairs). The Wattle House still stands today.

Findon Fair became the annual event for the sale of Southdown sheep, held on 14 September regardless of the day of the week, and there was also a Lamb Fair held on 12 July. By 1835 there were 3000 sheep for sale and the event had become the village's great annual funfair and also the statute fair for the hiring of labourers and farm servants.

Towards the end of the nineteenth century, a major revolution in the style of buying and selling sheep was on the horizon, and the late Mr Clement Fowler FRICS, who joined the auctioneers H. J. Burt & Sons in 1917 and became a partner in 1938 (he was also President of the Southdown Society in 1972), took up the story. He referred to an interesting book, *A Sussex Farmer*, written just before the Second World War by William Wood, who farmed at Park Farm, Twineham, and wrote about life in the Sussex countryside in the latter part of the nineteenth century. Describing the many fairs and markets which he attended as a young man, Wood said:

> Here again we see the changes time brings — the Auctioneer — there was very strong objection to this change, the Flock Masters who had sold their own sheep for years hated the idea of handing them over to another man to sell, especially having to pay him for doing it, and this reform in marketing was a long time delayed by their opposition but it was a reform and therefore had to come eventually.

Wood went on to say that he attended the old fairs for many years and that sometimes, perhaps because of a dry summer and lack of feed, or bad times or lack of money, there was little trade and, time and time again, he would see sheep driven home after their owner had sat on the wattles all day and never had an offer for his stock. The bigger men, who had regular customers buying their lambs for years, always managed to sell, even when they had to take a poor price: it was the smaller flocks and the smaller men who were left behind. At other times, when sheep were in keen demand and trade was very fast, it was the buyers who suffered: some of them were unable to find sheep because the regular buyers from the big flock masters had the first offer and smaller customers went unserved.

Under a system of sale by auction, these disadvantages would disappear: all the sheep would be offered and bid for and would make their value on the day, whether or not they came from a known owner. Every buyer would have the chance to bid and buy, whether attending for the first time or for the fortieth, and the only condition demanded would be the ability to pay for the purchase.

In about 1886, Henry James Burt (usually known as Harry Jas.

Burt) established the Steyning firm of auctioneers which in due course would become Churchman Burt & Sons. Ten years later he approached the larger flock masters in the county suggesting that he might auction their sheep on their behalf, in place of the time-honoured method of private bargain. He received some dusty answers: many of the old flock masters were opposed to what they considered to be the foolishness of paying another man to do what they could equally well do themselves. The replies Burt received included a letter dated 24 June 1896, from the Revd John Goring who said: 'If I sold by auction I should be content to let you do it for me, but I consider the practice so injurious that I feel it a duty to discourage rather than give in to it.' A gentleman from Rackham Farm, Pulborough, sent a postcard (it cost him a ha'penny) saying: 'Dear Sir, I am sorry but on principle I cannot accede to your wishes.' Slater, the bailiff for Mr Bridger of Old Erringham Farm, Old Shoreham, wrote: 'Sir, Mr Bridger, Esq, does not feel inclined for you to sell the sheep at Findon Fair,' Mr Alan Davey from Southwick (now a built-up area but with some good farms at the time) was a little less brusque, though perhaps his choice of phrase was unfortunate: 'Dear Sir, I shall sell myself if I can. Hoping you are well.' There was a cryptic card from Mr A. Short, who farmed the whole of Findon: 'Dear Sir, Thank you for your cheque received this morning. I am sorry too.'

Harry Burt persevered and, in accordance with what was no doubt a countrywide trend, he did start earning his commission by selling by auction at Findon in 1896. Within a very short time he took over the whole Fair, including the management and collection of tolls, which he paid over to the Holfords, who in turn settled with the Lord of the Manor.

The Sheep Fair grew bigger. In 1921 Mr Frank Holford retired but his family still had the rights of hiring and firing at Findon, and Holford's son negotiated a new ten-year lease giving Burt the exclusive right to sell the sheep at the main Sheep Fair and the July Lamb Fair. The Holfords retained ownership of the wattles, and repaired and stored them, but Burt's firm pitched them. This transitional arrangement lasted until 1926, when the Holfords relinquished their rights in favour of Colonel Margesson, Lord of the Manor. The auctioneers then purchased the wattles and other tackle and were reappointed to run the fairs and pay the tolls direct to the Lord of the Manor.

When the Colonel died in 1938, he bequeathed his rights to Findon

Parish Council, which also took over the Wattle House and still retains manorial rights concerning the Fair. The wattles are still stored in the Wattle House and in another building on the fairground.

Clem Fowler's first Findon Fair was in 1917, a time when all the sheep were driven to the Fair on foot, and he remembered them coming over the hill 'like small clouds' in the mist of the dawn, though they were often driven over the day before and were laid in local fields. Drovers from the Chichester area made up droves of up to 3000 sheep after the sale and drifted them over the Downs towards Amberley, Chichester and the Hampshire border, dropping lots off here and there at the farms of various purchasers.

In 1925 the firm decided that rail transport must be arranged for long-distance purchasers. It was not practical to drive large numbers of sheep down the road to Worthing and instead they were drifted over the Downs to the station at Steyning. In that first year one drift was marked up and sent over the hill during the afternoon of the Fair to lay up in meadows close to the town; another was taken over in the early evening, and a third drift was made up in the late evening and laid up on the hill. Large sorting pens were pitched at Steyning Market, right next to the railway station where Southern Railway provided a special shunting engine and fifty-six trucks to transport the thirty consignments of sheep to their new farms, far and wide. Later, when the trade was at its peak, up to eighty trucks were loaded (the job took two days) and even in 1947 fifty trucks were railed. It was the highlight of the year for the chosen local lads who were invited to help.

In 1928 the first lorry came on the scene at Findon, from a local contractor, though most of the sheep continued to use their own legs to and from the fairground. By the mid-1950s road transport had taken over and the rail trade had completely petered out by the time Dr Beeching closed the Steyning line.

The only period during which the Fair left Findon was in the dark wartime days. In 1940 the Fair had almost been pitched when the regional commissioner for the War Office issued an order, just a week before 14 September, saying that the site was too close to the coast and could be a prime target for a German air attack. Clem Fowler quickly searched for a suitable inland site and made an arrangement with Alfred Pankhurst, landlord of the Tabby Cat at West Grinstead, for the use of two fields next to the pub. It was no doubt very good for the landlord's trade, and it was quite convenient for the auctioneers as the site was handy for West Grinstead station and there were plenty of grass fields nearby for laying up the sheep before and after the Fair. All the tackle was hastily taken into the Weald on trailers drawn by traction engines belonging to the Harris family, who had always been responsible for the funfair held at the same time as the Sheep Fair. The Fair remained at West Grinstead until it returned to Nepcote Green in 1947.

In the late 1950s it was decided to change the date of the Fair. The old fixed date of 14 September frequently clashed with regular markets held elsewhere in Sussex so that it was often difficult to arrange motor transport and labour, and it was agreed to hold future Fairs on the second Saturday in September instead. Because it was a Charter fair, a special application had to be made to the Home Office for the necessary Order under the Fairs Act, which proved quite complicated but was successful.

The records in the offices of Churchman Burt (now Geering) give plenty of information about the sales of sheep at Findon over the years since 1910 (the records from 1896 to 1910 were destroyed) and it seems that numbers have been quite consistent. Between 1910 and 1918 the numbers of ewes and lambs sold varied between 6000 and 8250; from 1918 to 1922 they averaged 6500. At that time, as in the eighteenth and nineteenth centuries, most of the sheep were Southdowns but very few were rams. The first specialist ram sale at Findon was in 1923 and they were all Southdowns. From 1926 to 1931 the numbers averaged 9350 but the rams averaged only 115. In 1929 there were about 10 000 sheep and Findon was one of the biggest fairs in south-east England: that was the year of the dispersal of the Cissbury flock, with many of its ewes bred to Broadreed rams. The following year, with similar numbers, wether lambs from the Sompting flock took top prices at eighty shillings (i.e. £4).

1950 was an exceptional year when a total of 16 700 ewes and lambs and 1000 rams were sold, but otherwise numbers remained much the same as in the 1930s. There were still perhaps 10 000 sheep in 1974, when people came from all over England and Wales to buy and sell at one of the best fairs in the country. In recent years there has been a noticeable increase in the numbers of young ewes sold for breeding and a reduction in older draft ewes; and a very welcome change has been the increase in the number of rams sent for breeding, now about 500 a year.

Sadly, very few of them are now Southdowns. The proportion of the breed at its own major fair has been steadily decreasing since the 1920s. In the 1960s Southdown rams were still much in demand at Findon for crossing to produce fast-maturing, stocky lambs but today the great majority of rams sold at Findon are Suffolks — a breed with a considerable ancestral debt to the Southdown. By the 1980s only 10% of the rams and, even more dramatically, only 1% of the ewes sold at Findon were Southdowns.

In the early days Findon's July Lamb Fair was very popular with the flock masters on the South Downs, who would dispose of a fair proportion of their lambs on weaning because they did not have adequate grass or green crops to carry them through until the Great Fair in September. At one time there would be nearly 4000 lambs offered at the July Fair but the Southdown flocks started to decrease after the First World War, with the downland being broken up for cereal crops. By 1971 only 400 lambs were offered and the Lamb Fair was discontinued.

Findon Great Fair is still a major sheep event and buyers come for all over southern England. Ram puchasers come from as far as Devon and Cornwall and in some years groups of buyers have come from the Midlands and Lancashire as well as the eastern counties. It is a great social occasion within the farming community and is still pitched in the traditional manner, using cleft chestnut wattles, up on Nepcote Green fairground in its beautiful South Downs setting. As well as being a day of hard business, it remains a highly picturesque occasion which has caught the attention of the television cameras more than once in recent years. But those who knew the Fair's bumper years in the 1920s, when Barclay Wills bore witness, will be saddened that so few of the sheep at Findon today are of the local Southdown breed. Arthur Young would not be able to believe his eyes.

CHAPTER TWELVE

The Future of the Southdown: Breeders' Views

These views, given by a wide cross-section of Southdown breeders and presented here without prejudice, highlight many of the breed's qualities and also give an idea of the healthy differences of opinion within the Society today. That there are such differences shows that there is no dangerous complacency and will act as a positive spur to the future prosperity of an exceptional and exciting breed.

- The breed has improved immensely during the post-war years. Now the demand for Southdown crossing rams is only for good long sheep, standing tall enough to cover a big ewe; and this sort of ram loses the satisfying beauty of the chubby, meaty, old-fashioned hind leg. So most of us try to breed what the market wants and what we best sell — even if we do not like the shape so much.

- As a Southdown breeder for the last 14 years, living in south-west Scotland, I have found that the main role of the breed here is crossing with the Scotch Mule hogg. With this in mind, the easy lambing ability is important and must be maintained or even improved on. The importation of either French or New Zealand blood must be carefully done so that the easy lambing ability is not lost, while at the same time improving the growth rate and producing a leaner carcase to meet the modern market. The wool staple could be a bit longer, making the wool more valuable.

- I perceive there to be two distinct types of Southdown in current vogue. There is the short-legged, blocky, broad-chested, traditional type which at its best has fine wool, a great back end, rather darker but even-coloured nose. This type matures very rapidly and can run to fat if not appropriately managed. The second type is longer, taller and stays lean more easily. The wool tends to be less dense and the nose colour lighter and often uneven. The second type is thought to be more attractive to the commercial farmer as a crossing ram while the smaller-looking type actually has the better conformation. It might seem that the ideal would be to attempt to breed a hybrid having all the good features of both types but it looks very much as if each type tends to breed true, almost as if they are two separate breeds. It looks suspiciously to me as if the few New Zealand Southdowns imported to Britain have come to look as they do as a result of some non-pedigree 'improvement'. My feeling about further importations are therefore that any stock now imported should be selected from animals larger than but of the same stamp as the traditional, blocky type.

- The New Zealand imports were alleged to be for size increase though many competent authorities remain unconvinced that the New Zealand Southdown has anything to offer. Certainly, new blood lines can be a good thing for a breed with fairly small flock size. Many people feel that very good examples can be found in Australia, France and the USA.

- I view the future with reasonable long-term confidence. In the production of sheepmeat, conformation is going to count; and that is what we have got. There will be changes in grading methods from the present rather hit-and-miss arrangements. If meat is to hold its place on the country's menus, quality must be improved — not just on elimination of cull cow and continental beef but also an end to large hoggets sold as lamb!

- Wonderful meat. I am breeding for prolificacy and growth, keeping what I consider a typical Southdown look and conformation. Beware of inbreeding and where rams come from, always culling anything which has hereditary faults. The advantages of Southdowns are their size, their ability to thrive and remain contented in a small area, and the flavour of their meat, and nowadays the advisability of using the rams as terminal sires on ewe lambs of other breeds. It would be good if all twin lambs reached 16 kg deadweight off grass at six months and possibly one could achieve this by retaining larger ewes for breeding. The size of the lamb is important as the penalties do not encourage any 'fat'. I do not know whether the introduction of New Zealand blood has increased the length of the Southdown but I understood this was one of the hopes. Conformation being all important, I think we have to take great care with importations and I wonder whether it is possible to keep up the superb quality? It is up to each breeder to be vigilant in culling and to study pedigrees to prevent inbreeding which would bring hereditary problems. I feel size of carcase is the concern at present but is it so important to get them much larger? Will larger rams give us breeding problems? There are plenty of other breeds (especially Down breeds) which produce larger carcases. I think from the market point of view our aim should be to get a good lamb of 16 kg from between four to six months, without fat; keeping the characteristics of the Southdown, remembering their use for clearing-up operations, and making such good use of rough areas.

- By sensible management, suiting the known characteristics of the breed, excellent carcases can be produced, matching *exactly* the current demand for small, high conformation lamb. The bloodlines already in the country are adequate for this purpose and no new importations are needed. Care must be taken that we do not lose what we have (which is excellent) chasing after some 'simple' answer to our problems, e.g. by outcrossing.

- We 'zoo-keepers' who have more than one breed aspire to be commercial farmers but find it a struggle, what with having to earn a living and all. I believe that some of us are producing good stock (see us at the Royal Show, for example) and many of us are promoting the breed far from the South Downs and introducing it to the ignorant. I show at Newark, Leicester, Peterborough, Derby and occasionally in Buckinghamshire and Bedfordshire, but I'm almost the sole supporter. Where is the selling thrust for Southdowns? Not up here, I assure you, unless I do it. No wonder we are overlooked. The Society is expanding and strengthening all the time. Surely we could afford a levy to help promote a little bit more professionally than we do? I bet that if we renamed the Southdown 'Dessous-de-Sud' or 'Wooldebeest' and alleged it was imported at huge expense from Benelux, it would catch on in no time!

- There is no general agreement among Southdown breeders as to the type of sheep which they are striving to evolve. This is due to a lack of pressure from consumers and purchasers as to what they might want. Many Southdown breeders are striving to evolve a bigger sheep with a higher milking potential and twin lambs of viable birthweight. Lambs should sell 'fat' from their mothers, without weaning, at 12 to 14 weeks old. The now old-fashioned tiny Southdown is useless for pure breeding or for cross-breeding. There is no need to lose quality with larger sized Southdowns, and there is reason to believe, from photographs, that the turn-of-the-century Southdown was relatively large. There is a comparison between the Aberdeen-Angus cattle and the Southdown sheep. Both species produce(d) the highest quality meat. Responding to demands for a small fleshy joint, both breeds were selected from for small animals. The resulting semi-dwarf offspring nearly ruined both breeds. The Aberdeen-Angus breeders saw their error in time and reacted accordingly. The Southdown breeders ignored matters and relegated their sheep to minority status.

- There is considerable interest in the longer, large New Zealand type of Southdown, particularly for use on ewe hoggs. Unfortunately Southdown rams do not command the high prices of some other breeds: the highest price realised has been 301 guineas at Wilton in 1983 — for crossing.

- The New Zealand have the eye-muscle but sometimes they have not got the leg. And they are losing the characteristic density of the traditional Southdown's fleece — the coat is too open. But some of the New Zealand lines now in Australia are cracking good ones, with back ends like the traditional English type but as big as donkeys!

- I feel we should endeavour to maintain numbers and try to breed for today's market, i.e. sheep with good length and good fleshing qualities which, when crossed with our commercial sheep, will produce lambs without excessive fat cover. A further importation of rams could be beneficial to increase our genetic pool, providing they were good specimens of the breed. I hope the breed will be with us for many more years and will contribute to the production of good mutton for both home and abroad.

- The main opportunity for the Southdown ram in the future, other than for pure breeding, is likely to be as a terminal sire on ewe hoggs, where the lower birthweight of the lamb, compared to other Down crosses, puts less stress on the ewe.

- I feel that with the housewife requiring small, quality meat joints the Southdown is bound to flourish, especially as their upkeep requirements are so small. Their 150% lambing is very good for a Down breed and you can get up to 200% if you are a very good manager and put teaser rams out. They are very docile and don't get out, nor do they eat much (so be careful not to get them too fat — put them on a quarter of an acre and starve them, then flush for the tup). I don't castrate and I sell on the hook because then they grade and get heavier and leaner — very nice carcases of quality meat. No particular problems with lambing; no foot rot or anything.

- There *is* a market. Good small lamb, 16–17 kg — the main thing is that the lamb is small at birth, it isn't a hungry lamb and doesn't need as much milk as a Suffolk and they don't draw on the ewe lambs so much. Very easy to lamb. You need to know your strains: some get fatter more quickly than others and are too fat if taken to too heavy a weight, but then any animal will get fat if you keep it too long. Showing is very important for the breed and those with larger flocks should contribute to a big line-up — publicity is the problem and the breed needs money and forceful people behind its promotion. I'm wary of the New Zealand imports: they were bred to do a job in New Zealand and the ones I've seen in this country are bigger sheep, with a lot more daylight underneath, and have lost the hindquarter — and it is the hindquarter that is the Southdown's trademark. There could also be lambing problems, nor have you got the wool: the coat is flatter and very white. But a lot of Southdowns went to France in the 1950s and there should be a good gene pool there.

- The Southdown needs to look more to the future. In the old days there was more pure-breeding: you bred pure Southdown lambs.

Then transport improved so that you can now move thousands of sheep down from, say, Scotland, and now the lamb market is nearly all crosses.

- One of the benefits of the breed is that they don't eat much and they don't need good land. You can stock more heavily and the management is much easier than for other breeds. The wool is very fine but there is little of it. For no particular reason, I'd think that the short, stocky type would tend to be fatter than the long and lean, but you must sell at the right weight to avoid them getting too fat. The longer body tends to lose the gigot and you don't want them too sharp in the shoulder as terminal sires: the Mule is already sharp in the shoulder.

- There are some flocks in which the sheep have a lot of food pumped into them: they look reasonable but waste away in other flocks, going backwards rather than going on.

- I'm not particularly impressed by the French Southdowns but perhaps only because they show them badly! Perhaps they are not very good on registration or keeping the breed pure.

- There is a place for the smaller sheep in the future, especially in Europe now that subsidies are on the ewe instead of variable premiums on the lamb. The Southdown is ideal on ewe hoggs in their first breeding season, or ewe lambs 7–9 months old up to the tup: the lambs are smaller and don't pull a young ewe down so much.

  They are cheap to keep — they don't need much fencing. And they are the fastest at producing early lambs. The New Zealand type have the length; they are producing an early quality lamb, which is what we should do. There seem to be two camps within the society but we must all pull together with a co-ordinated publicity effort for the sake of the breed.

  The Southdown will produce a good shoulder, good neck and good leg. It's ideal for the high-speed family butcher: chop-chop, bang-bang, and the whole sheep is ready and the whole lot can be eaten. What with the supermarket problems like listeria, it's much better to get your meat cut and boned at the local butcher so that you know where it has been. And the quality of the Southdown over the last eight years has been of a very high standard: steps are being taken now to make it a commercial breed again. I agree with the stamp — it is the quality sheep with everything, but it must meet modern requirements in a bigger frame and still have the quality wool and quality leg.

- Commercially useless. Hopeless mothers. Great as pets. Can't give them away.

- Excellent for crossing. Good temperament and hardy.

- Must shed the small fatty image and promote true potential to commercial farmers. Must move with the times to survive in the future, with ever-increasing continental breeds.

- More docile than a commercial flock.

- A pleasure to keep: placid, hardy, cross well with other breeds. We use the ram on Suffolk and Jacob ewes — beautiful lambs.

- Ideal size for smallholders. Very difficult to sell.

- Excellent proportion of meat to bone. Very good flavour — nothing like it. Very fast maturing lambs, good growth rate.

- Quiet and reliable breed, very underestimated terminal sire, with great potential for the future.

- There is still a place for the Southdown in crossbreeding for early lambs, and the breed is very good for putting on any lambs. Might be a revival now that there is a 21 kg limit on variable premium.

- Good lambs for lightweight classes. Winning many lightweight classes in local fatstock shows, and champion for many years.

- Docile, easy to handle, heavy stocking rates, fast maturing, excellent flavour. Needs an overall size increase, and decrease in fat, through selective breeding. Ought we to consider embryo transplants of our best stock to attain increase in size and leanness?

- Excellent docile sheep, very easy to handle and control. Ewes get too fat if not starved after lambs taken off.

- Our Southdowns are used therapeutically with maladjusted young children — docility and friendliness very important.

- A producer of premium quality lambs but whilst quantity remains the main requirement of the market its commercial role is limited mainly to that of a sire for use on commercial ewe lambs.

- Excellent sire of young quality lambs. Export market for carcases should be encouraged.

- Fleece and carcase winner at several major shows. A breed we must keep going for the quality of meat and wool, and forget about some of the imported sheep coming into this country.

- Very docile, and do well on any grass. Very good for crossing with ewe lambs of lean breeds. The very best flavour and tender lambs to eat.

- Docile and manageable, especially for a woman. Tender, lean meat. Early maturing.

- The breed is hardy and, due to progressive breeding policy, still provides lambs of high quality for the meat trade. Small bones, well fleshed. Very profitable for sheep kept per acre and easily managed with minor fencing requirements.

- Easy to handle. Do well on 'poor', 'old-fashioned' grassland (the farm is lowland, poor acid grassland ranging from dry gravel to wet peaty soils). Need very careful extra feeding for lambing and a 24-hour watch at lambing time to avoid heavy losses. Very difficult to shear but good price for the wool. Good meat classification (3L) when using ram on small or old ewes of other breeds. Southdown x Southdown also good meat (3L) if carefully weighed and sent when ready at 32.5–35 kg, otherwise too fat.

- Used for grazing beneath Kentish cobnut trees and have proved perfect for grazing of nut platts as well as providing a blocky and lean carcase.

- Very good all-round sheep.

- Very convenient, manageable sheep for the amateur. Live sheep and mutton admired by visitors.

- A satisfying type to keep. The 'older type' preferable. In my view the major problem facing the breed is that, with a large number of flocks with few sheep each, may cause a loss in conformation standards due to difficulties in assessing really good rams — a major snag for the small-flock folk.

- A limited future for quality light lambs under 16.5 kg from ewe lambs.

- Easy to handle, placid, good finishing. Economical and generally a pleasure to have.

- Produced quality fat lamb with the right balance of fat to lean for tasty meat. Important to keep the unique genetics evolved over centuries of breeding, rather than short-term fashion.

- Weight in a small package. Excellent cross on halfbred hoggets. Easy shepherding. Superb carcase and first-class flavour.

- Small size ideal for freezer meat. After initial teething troubles (started with old ewes), have become increasingly impressed. Thrifty and hardy little sheep. Good mothers and the meat quality is superb. Intend to increase the flock as they are ideal for our land on chalk of North Downs. Southdowns will become our main flock — I like them!

- Very placid, friendly and docile. Good lawn-mowers but tendency to get rather fat. Good taste.

- Good natured but a bit wriggly to handle when foot-trimming.

- Docile, economical, reliable: connoisseur's meat; excellent grazers. All lambs sold fat graded E3L, E3H, U2, U3L, R2, R3.

- Attractive, easy to shepherd, profitable and adaptable.

- Small flock kept purposely to represent traditional Sussex breed amongst museum's collection of reconstructed historic buildings in south east England.

- Very easy to manage without a dog. Don't climb out of the field. I like them! Ram put to Clun ewes produces excellent carcases for the butcher.

- I think there is a future if the breed can get bigger — length and good gigots are most important. More interest in smaller breeds likely when the variable premium is replaced by ewe premium.

- Amazingly placid and good doers in wet or dry conditions on heavy clay. Not very prolific.

- Excellent meat, very quick to finish. Rams good for crossing for earlier finishing in other breeds. Also top premium for wool.

- Very good.

- Fantastic.

APPENDIX ONE

Breed Description and Scale of Points

	General character and appearance	
HEAD	Wide, level between the ears, with no sign of slug or dark poll.	
FACE	Full, not too long from eyes to nose, and of one even mouse colour, not approaching black or speckled; under jaw light.	
EYES	Large, bright and prominent.	
EARS	Of medium size, and covered with short wool.	
NECK	Wide at base, strong and well set on to the shoulder.	
CARRIAGE	Corky legs, short, straight, and of one even mouse colour, and set on outside of body.	

TOTAL 30

SHOULDERS	Well set, the top level with the back.
CHEST	Wide and deep.
BACK	Level, with a wide flat loin.

RIBS	Well sprung, and well ribbed up, thick through the heart, with fore and hind flanks fully developed.
RUMP	Wide and long, and well turned.
TAIL	Large, and set on almost level with the chine.
LEGS OF MUTTON	Full, well let down, with a deep, wide twist (including thighs).

TOTAL 50

WOOL	Of fine texture, great density, and of sufficient length of staple, covering the whole of the body down to the hocks and knees, and right up to the cheeks, with a full foretop, but not round the eyes, or across the bridge of the nose.
SKIN	Of a delicate bright pink.

TOTAL 20

―――
100

Breed Societies

CLIVE PRITCHARD
SOUTHDOWN LODGE
300 COPLE ROAD
CARDINGTON
BEDFORD   MK44 3SH
0234-838807

SOUTHDOWN SHEEP SOCIETY
Secretary: C. B. Pritchard, BA
45 Commercial Road
Bedford, MK40 1QS
Tel. Bedford (0234) 56227

AMERICAN SOUTHDOWN BREEDERS' ASSOCIATION
Secretary-Treasurer: Gary Jennings
HCR 13, Box 220
Fredonia, Texas 76842
Tel. (915) 429-6226

ASSOCIATION DES ÉLEVEURS FRANÇAIS DE SOUTH-DOWN
Cidex 9058—Bel-Air—Saint-Victor
03410 DOMÉRAT
Tel. 70 05 48 39

THE SOUTHDOWN SHEEP SOCIETY OF NEW ZEALAND INC.
PO Box 636
Palmerston North
Auckland Building
Society House
475 Main Street
Tel. 84-163

AUSTRALIAN SOCIETY OF BREEDERS OF BRITISH SHEEP
Secretary-Treasurer: H. T. C. Woodfull, OBE
Royal Show Grounds
Epsom Road
Ascot Vale
Victoria 3032
Tel. 33-0471

Bibliography

Barclay Wills' The Downland Shepherds Edited by Richard Pailthorpe and Shaun Payne, illustrated by Gordon Beningfield (Alan Sutton, 1989)

Baxter's Library of Agriculture and Horticultural Knowledge, With a Memoir of Mr. Ellman, Late of Glynde 3rd edition, 1834

Coke of Norfolk and His Friends (2 volumes) A. M. W. Stirling (John Lane, the Bodley Head 1908)

Farming For Export Lamb P. G. Stevens (Southdown Sheep Society of New Zealand)

Races Ovines Giles Perret (Institut Technique de l'Elevage Ovin et Caprin)

The Showman Shepherd David Turner (Farming Press, 1990)

The Southdown (American Southdown Breeders' Association, 1982)

The Southdown Sheep E. Walford Lloyd (Southdown Sheep Society, 1st edition 1922, 3rd edition 1936)

English Folk: A Book of Characters Wallace Nutestein (Jonathan Cape, 1938)

The Webbs of Streetly and Babraham E. Walford Lloyd (private MS)

Victoria County History (Sussex) Edited by T. P. Hudson (Vol. VI, 1980)

Articles in *The Ark* (published monthly by Rare Breeds Survival Trust, NAC, Stoneleigh, for its members):

Hall, Stephen J. G.: The Southdown sheep: development and conservation (June 1989)

Wade-Martins, Susanna: Thomas William Coke and livestock breeding at Holkham (August 1986)

Wakeham-Dawson, P., MA Dip. Agric. (Cantab.): The Southdown sheep (August 1988)

OTHER ARTICLES

Jones, John L.: Southdown sheep for quality (*Country Life*, 28 June 1979)

Churchill, Penny: Southdown (*The Sheep Farmer*, September/October 1985)

Farrant, Sue: John Ellman of Glynde in Sussex (*The Agricultural History Review*, Vol. 26 1978, Pt II)

Whitmore, Richard: Jonas Webb of Babraham (*Cambridgeshire and Huntingdonshire Life*)

Croston, D., with A. J. Kempster, D. R. Guy, D. W. Jones: Growth and carcass characteristics of crossbred lambs by ten sire breeds compared at the same carcass subcutaneous fat proportion (*Anim. Prod.* 1987, Vol. 44: 83–106)

Hudson, T. P.: Findon Market and Fair in the Middle Ages (West Sussex Archives Society Journal, January 1978)

Acknowledgements

Many present and past members of the Southdown Sheep Society have contributed their views and information about their flocks to this book, and several have also given invaluable details about the breed's history since the Second World War. In particular, the Society is grateful to Mr Hugh T. Clark (Centenary President), the Rt Hon the Lord Harvington (Foreword), Mr John Thorley (Introduction), Mr Peter Clementson (wool production), Mr David Humphrey (commercial management), Mr Paul Wakeham-Dawson (history), Mrs Sheila Colman and Mr Philip Whitcombe (the Southdown overseas), and Mr Richard Pailthorpe and Mr Shaun Payne (shepherds). Gratitude is most certainly due to the American Southdown Breeders' Association, the New Zealand Southdown Sheep Society and also Mr Geoff Baker in Australia for their co-operation and submission of papers for the book.

Thanks are due, too, to the West Sussex Record Office, the East Sussex County Records Office, the Meat and Livestock Commission, the British Wool Marketing Board and Messrs Churchman Burt & Sons (Geerings). Above all the Society is grateful to the sponsors who have supported its Centenary celebration (including the production of this book), especially West Sussex County Council, the Society of Sussex Downsmen, Messrs Strutt & Parker of Lewes and, finally, to the Weald and Downland Open Air Museum at Singleton, who generously undertook the book's picture research, publishing and marketing and whose expertise has been invaluable.

The Society wishes to thank the following for financial support in publishing this book:

The Rt Hon. The Lord
  Harvington of Nantwich, AE
Mr R. Backshall
Mr D. W. Baker
Mr A. Baker
Mr P. Ballard
T. Bannister & Company
Mr P. J. Bircher
Mrs J. Bradshaw
Mr F. W. Brand
Mr L. McL. Brown
Mr and Mrs A. Bull
Mr D. G. Burden
Miss A. J. Burtenshaw
Mr R. J. Cave
Mr G. Chapman
Mr H. T. Clark
Mr P. A. Clementson
Mrs S. Colman
Mr S. J. Cook
Mr W. H. Corney
Mrs M. Covey
Messrs J. and M. Craig
Mr R. Dearnley
Mr D. Dingle
Miss S. Dupree
Mr M. W. E. Dzenis
Mr K. Fellows
Mr and Mrs W. H. Fox
Mr J. R. Friend
Mr and Mrs J. D. Goode
Mr S. Gradden
Mr F. H. Grantham
Mr A. M. Hack
P. M. and S. M. Hack
Mr M. Hammersley

Mr R. J. Hammond
Mr J. Harpwood
Mr and Mrs A. R. Harris
Mr R. M. Harris
Marion Hart
Mr J. Mark Hawtin
Mrs Joan Hayes
Mr Joe Henson
Messrs Hobbs Parker
The late Mr J. F. Holdstock
Mr G. M. Hommerstone
Mr J. Mansel Hopkin
The Revd and Mrs D. M. Hopkins
Mrs C. Hornung
Mr A. L. Hughes
Mrs F. J. Hughes
Messrs J. and D. Humphrey
Mr C. G. F. Ing
F. I. and P. A. Jordan
Mr G. C. D. Keane
Mr C. G. King
Mr Michael Lampson
Mr B. J. M. Larkin
Mr Charles Laurie
Mrs V. Maxwell
Mr and Mrs P. Mayes
Mrs A. C. McCall
Mr D. S. A. McDougall
Mr P. McLeod Smith
Mrs D. P. A. Millard
Mr F. K. Mitchell, TD
Mr J. Monks
Mr T. J. Morgan
Mr P. A. Mummery
Mr N. R. W. Munson
Mr C. Ower

Miss H. J. Paynter
Mr and Mrs J. E. M. Phillips
J. G. and D. G. Pond
Mr Robert Pool
Mrs S. L. Renner
J. & R. M. Rowe & Sons
Mr M. P. Sadler
Mr Bertram Sample, BSc.
Messrs Sandys
Mrs J. A. Scott
Mr J. R. D. Sears
Mr Donald Sherlock
Mrs K. P. Short
Mr Michael Shove, JP, FRICS
Mr A. Smith
Mr and Mrs M. F. Sprake
Mrs M. Steele
Mr K. Stevenson

Mr C. J. H. Sykes
Mrs S. M. Thomson
Dr. D. C. Turner
Mrs C. Wadland
Messrs Wakeham Dawson &
  Harmer
Mr Paul Wakeham Dawson
Mrs P. A. Walford
Mrs T. Warnock
Weald and Downland Open Air
  Museum
Mr M. R. Weston
Mr and Mrs H. A. W. Wheeldon
Mr P. A. Whitcombe
Miss N. Winter
Mr Cyril Wise
Claire Worden

J. Anseen Animal Health, Wantage, Oxon
Dengie Feeds, Southminster, Essex
Dewi James & Co., Rhoshill, Cardigan, Dyfed
Mr E. John, Intervet UK Ltd, Cambridge
Leigh Thomas & Co. Ltd, Newport, Isle of Wight
National Westminster Bank plc
Oriel Jones & Sons, Llanybydder, Dyfed
Park Davis Research Laboratories, Pontypool
The Rt Hon. The Lord Ross of Newport, FRICS
Tinsley Wire Sheffield Ltd, Sheffield

Index